THE DILWORTH STORY

Richard M. Dilworth

THE

DILWORTH

STORY

The Biography of *RICHARD DILWORTH*
Pioneer Developer of the Diesel Locomotive

FRANKLIN M. RECK

McGRAW-HILL BOOK COMPANY, INC.
New York Toronto London

THE DILWORTH STORY

Library of Congress Catalog Card Number: 54-12259

Published by the McGraw-Hill Book Company, Inc.

Printed in the United States of America

CONTENTS

ILLUSTRATIONS

FOREWORD

I first became acquainted with Dick Dilworth when he and H. L. Hamilton were working on gasoline-electric rail cars, and I was impressed then with something in his character that seems to me to have carried on clear through his remarkable career.

Dick was convinced that certain inherent advantages of the internal-combustion engine indicated that it was destined for an important place in American railroading. He had gone about as far as he could with the gasoline and distillate engine, and the results were not too satisfactory. Several companies had given up on attempts to build internal-combustion-engine-powered cars and trains. The feeling that it just wasn't the way to run trains was deeply rooted among engineers. It was so deeply rooted that on the very eve of the spectacular initial success of the Diesel engine on United States railroads one of the great locomotive companies actually published an advertisement which said: "Come what may . . . steam designs are ready to meet every demand of our railroads with the least amount of experimentation" and, later, "and the same factors . . . will continue to keep steam the dominating power for railroad transportation for a long, long time to come."

The streak in Dick's character which made him successful

in a field where so many others had failed was a refusal to
be licked just because something wouldn't run right the first
few years. He and H. L. Hamilton had worked out most of
the problems of how to take the power of the internal-
combustion engine from the shaft to rails, but they lacked the
kind of prime mover that would do a main-line job. When a
Diesel engine that appeared to have the right characteristics
came along, Dick was willing to give it a try—despite the
dismal history of earlier efforts along the same line. The rest
is history.

Dick Dilworth, unlike some engineers, was not hampered
by preconceived notions so fixed that they kept him from
recognizing something of value. Perhaps the way Dick grew
up had something to do with this. I suspect there were times
in his life when he literally would not have eaten regularly
if he had not been in the habit of trying something new when
the old wouldn't work.

Charles F. Kettering

THE DILWORTH STORY

Chapter 1

THE EDUCATION OF AN ENGINEER

What do you want to write my story for?" Dick Dilworth asks. "If it's for my friends, most of them are gone. If it's for the generation now taking over, they don't give a damn."

Dilworth's bluntness of speech and saltiness of language are legendary in railroad circles. He has called railroad presidents names never used by salesmen. He has driven home his points with parables for men only. He has slaughtered sacred cows and shattered tradition. He is no respecter of persons, least of all himself, and he has a horror of glorification.

Historians look at the record and say, rightly, that Dilworth put together the first successful Diesel high-speed passenger locomotives, that he presided over the creation of the first Diesel freight locomotives, and that today Dilworth locomotives are highballing down all the nation's main lines.

While all this is perfectly true, in Dilworth's mind it doesn't give the right picture of his part in the drama. He wants it understood that the Diesel locomotive was not a sudden conception, but a growth. It didn't happen all at once, but gradually. While it was happening, nobody clearly visualized the end result. There were days of bafflement, disappointment, and futility. A development was undertaken because it seemed like a good idea at the time. This led to another development, sometimes a wrong one. As the groping went on, a revolutionary new idea was taking shape, the outlines of which nobody clearly saw.

Throughout all this struggle, Dilworth—whose heart is with the sea where he spent many of the formative years of his adventurous life—was the man at the steering oar, guiding the development away from the rocks and the shoals. His function was not to make inventions that pushed the Diesel along, but to steer it along the course it wanted to go. And in the early days, when the seas were high, the job of steering was like manning the sweep of a whaleboat, a sweaty, hand-powered task without benefit of diamond gear, steering engine, or any other form of irreversible control.

Thus, whenever an enthusiast oversimplifies history by saying that Dilworth "invented the Diesel locomotive," he quotes a line from Bobby Burns:

"My mother was a canteen lassie. Any one of a troop of dragoons was my father."

He wants it clearly understood that the Diesel locomotive had many fathers.

This point out of the way, Dilworth reminds you that his story is the testimony of a single witness and that no story written from the viewpoint of one man can be complete. He makes this clear with a story.

"You know," he says, pulling thoughtfully on a battered pipe, "a corporation was throwing a banquet to kiss an old-timer goodbye, and I had to make a speech. This old chap had been with the company since the beginning but had been more or less overlooked in recent years. The audience was full of young executives who thought they knew just how the corporation had grown to its present high estate, and I wanted to get across the idea that maybe the old-timer knew some things they didn't. So I invented this yarn to make my point:

"Out on the West Coast the Columbia River runs down to the sea. Up just beyond tidewater there's a dam—the Bonneville Dam. Now the Columbia is a great salmon river, and salmon go up the river past the dam and into the tributaries—the Deschutes, the John Day, the Umatilla, and the Snake—and somewhere up one of these rivers the salmon spawns. Later the fingerlings start for the sea, and when they get to the Bonneville Dam they wait until a flood carries them over the top. Now, if you were to take a dipnet and shove it into the water above the dam and pull up a fish and ask him, 'Fish, where did all this water come from?' you'd get an answer. He was born on the Deschutes; so he knows all the water came from there. But if you dipped again and brought up another fish, you'd get another answer."

So Dilworth wants it made clear that, when he talks about himself and his part in evolving the Diesel locomotive, he's giving his own answer out of the currents of his own river. He knows that many streams contributed to the flood of Diesel transportation now coursing over the nation's rails, but he doesn't pretend familiarity with all of them. He was spawned on only one headwater, traveled one stream to the main river, and there followed the mixed waters of many streams to his destiny.

Early days

Richard McLean Dilworth was born in Seattle in the territory of Washington on March 6, 1885. He's reasonably certain of the date, but he wouldn't swear to it. Seattle was destroyed by fire in 1889, and such records as the territory kept were burned. Therefore, when it comes to establishing birth dates for passports and Social Security, Dilworth has had some difficulty in proving that he was born at all.

The future engineer's father, Richard Burch Dilworth, was a Presbyterian minister, assigned by the Board of Home Missions to preach in Seattle. As a youngster, Richard Dilworth had seen service in the Civil War, and after his discharge had taken a job acting as an armed guard on the Santa Fe Trail, protecting stage lines from Indians and bandits.

"Dad was a torpedo," Dick explains dryly, "using his gun to finance his way through the Princeton Theological School."

In the turbulent pioneer settlement of Seattle, the ministry was anything but a reflective occupation, nor was the salary such as to let a man of God spend much time contemplating the eternal verities. Dilworth Senior ran a tugboat during the week and used the tugboat on Sundays to collect a congregation. Roads along Puget Sound were practically nonexistent. Sunday mornings, the Reverend Mr. Dilworth cruised along the shore from village to village, taking the faithful aboard, then landing on some convenient beach for services.

Though young Dick was brought up in the family of a minister, the child's life could hardly be called sheltered. The environment that his young mind was called upon to comprehend was not that of a regulated society, but one of violence, adventure, and lusty action. The family didn't settle long enough for him to be enrolled in a school. They moved—or were driven—from town to town along the Northwest frontier.

When Dick was about five, his parents moved to Astoria, and here the Reverend Mr. Dilworth formed a strange alliance against the forces of evil. Astoria at the time was populated by Portuguese salmon fishermen. Whaling ships, bound north for the arctic, put in regularly at Astoria to fill out their crews, and their methods were unscrupulous.

"Crimps for the whalers would shanghai the Portuguese salmon fishermen," Dick recalls. "They'd get the poor fellows drunk—on their own money if possible—and deliver them aboard ship for forty dollars a head."

To combat this practice, Mr. Dilworth joined forces with the keeper of the biggest saloon and honky-tonk in Astoria, a man with the poetic name of Silas Lotus Jones. Valiantly these two partners battled the whalers and crimps, the man of God and the dive operator with a conscience, but in the end both men found Astoria beyond redemption.

When Dick was about ten, the saloonkeeper and preacher were forced to leave the lusty and unrepentant port.

"They were kicked out," Dick puts it. "Told to git, or else."

Together they moved to Roseburg in southern Oregon. There Jones set up two establishments known as the Roseleaf

and the Senate, while Mr. Dilworth organized his church.
They found Roseburg as sinful as Astoria. A cattle and sheep
war was in progress that was won by the cattlemen through
the effective process of shooting down the sheepmen. Bandits
waylaid the stages, and there were times when gunfire drowned
out the church bells. To combat these affairs the preacher and
saloonkeeper ran an outfit known as the Stranglers, an un-
official law-enforcement agency that meted out justice at the
end of a rope. Thus the Reverend Mr. Dilworth's time was
divided between the gun, the noose, and the Bible.

The boy remembered the time his father rode out with a
posse to track down a bandit. They were fired on from a clump
of bushes and returned the fire. When it was safe to advance
they strode behind the bushes and discovered lying there, well
riddled, a leading merchant of Roseburg, a prominent member
of Dilworth's congregation. Back in town they found the loot
from several robberies in the basement of his store.

Childhood days as rugged as these were not the kind to
compress a boy into any known mold. Neither in Astoria nor
in Roseburg was Dick enrolled in a school, and such education
as he came by he received at home, chiefly from his mother,
Mary Glover McLean Dilworth, who had taught school in
Kansas before her marriage.

Unhampered by such inhuman tyrannies as school and tru-
ant officers, young Dick had plenty of time in which to play
and grow strong for his years, and southwestern Oregon in the
1890s was a fine playground. It was a wild, new land, full of
antelope, bobcats, bear, and fish. There were steelhead trout
in Deer Creek and the South Umpqua, and these fabulous

fish Dick and his companions tamed with cane poles and live bait.

They made forays through the brush hunting for bear sign, and one day they came upon a tree marked a good 6 feet up by bear claws. This gave them the idea that if they were to get an ax and hoist one boy onto another's shoulders, bark could be scratched off a foot higher than the existing marks. Then, perhaps, some grownup would come along, see the fake claw marks, and comment in awe on the size of the bear. This they proceeded to do, exchanging conspiratorial grins at the fine deception.

A couple of days later they passed this tree again and noted claw marks almost 9 feet high—far higher than anything they could reach. Their minds visioned the size of the grizzly that must have done this, and the thought occurred that the big silvertip must still be in the neighborhood. They left hastily, glancing fearfully at every thicket, and never went back there again.

So Dilworth fished, hunted, and rebelliously studied reading and writing at home. He read whatever happened to be lying around. The first book he can recall digging into with any degree of faithfulness was Jules Verne's *Twenty Thousand Leagues under the Sea*. One of his companions could read newspapers glibly, and envy of this boy kept the reluctant Dick at his homework with moderate faithfulness.

Dilworth confesses to only one-half day of formal schooling in his entire life. One wonders how this man, without collegiate engineering training, could have contributed so vitally to the locomotives that have revolutionized American railroading. Part of the answer will be found in the roving and

undisciplined career pursued by Dilworth between the ages
of twelve and twenty-five. Part of the answer will never be
known until people can peer into the human mind and discover what mysterious things go on there.

Dilworth received his first and only half-day of classroom
schooling in 1897. In that year, memorable to Dilworth as the
year of McKinley's inauguration as President, his father was
ordered to New York City by the Presbyterian Board of Home
Missions to become a lecturer. The family moved into an old
brownstone house owned by the church. It was located at the
corner of Fifth Avenue and 12th Street, across the street
from the home of Theodore Roosevelt, who at that time was
Assistant Secretary of the Navy under McKinley.

The boy was enrolled at the public school, stayed for the
morning session, and walked out at noon, never to go back.

"During recess I got a licking from the boy who sat next to
me," Dilworth explains. "Then I got another licking from
the teacher for being in the fight. The double dose was too
much for me; so I ran away."

Footloose youngster

Dilworth insists on "drawing the mantle of charity"
over the next half dozen years. During that time he "stole the
trade of machinist," meaning that he was never apprenticed.
Leaving home as a twelve-year-old, big for his age and able to
take care of himself, he picked up odd jobs here and there and
learned to use tools by watching others.

Now and then he returned home, but never for long, and
the assumption is that the independent, headstrong youngster

couldn't stand the strict atmosphere of his father's household.

Yet, though his wild spirit could never be harnessed, the boy must have gained something valuable from his parents. In ordinary conversation Dilworth doesn't talk like a person of haphazard education, but rather like a man of background. He has no love of "fine" words but talks simply and with an ear for precise shades of meaning. Dick recalls that in Roseburg his father, with a preacher's faith in a classical education, made the boy study Latin. Much against his will, Dick waded through Julius Caesar's accounts of the Gallic wars and a book of Vergil. He hated it at the time, but he believes now that what he learned about the roots of words has remained with him.

"When you know that words have a history," he says, "you respect 'em."

His technical training is another matter. The following incident may throw light on the way Dilworth learned engineering. During those first years of vagabonding about the country, Dilworth was operating a lathe in the Westinghouse Machine Company in Pittsburgh. One of the jobs that came his way regularly was the boring of a tapered hole. It was a clearance hole and didn't have to be exact, but the inspector was fussy about it, and Dick invariably had great trouble setting up the machine in order to get it right. He had to "cut and try."

Then one time the man on the next machine got the job and Dick watched to see how he did it. Glancing out of the corner of his eye, he saw the man do some figuring with a pad and pencil, then refer to a little black book. Thereupon he took a bevel protractor, set up the compound rest on his lathe, bored his hole, and got it right the first time.

Dick discovered that the book was a machinist's handbook, but that to use it he would have to know trigonometry. When he tackled trigonometry, he found that he would have to go back and learn some arithmetic and geometry.

Later, at the same shop, he saw a man using a slide rule and asked him how he worked the thing. The man told him it was all based on logarithms—that what the slide rule did was add logarithms. Eager to use this short cut, Dick had to learn what a logarithm was, and he figures that he ended up by knowing more about the subject than a student who merely used a log table in a textbook.

Thus, though Dilworth never had an education fed to him by a recognized institution of learning at a standard rate of application, he never hesitated to tackle "book larnin' " whenever his job demanded it.

When Dilworth ran away from home after his double licking at the public school, he went across the Hudson River into New Jersey and wandered around, looking for someone who would take on a boy of twelve. He gravitated inevitably toward the Walter L. Main tent show, a one-ring circus, then playing in a small town the name of which Dilworth no longer remembers. The circus, traditional haven for fugitives from organized society, put the boy to work setting up seats for the audience.

He stayed with the show for some months, finally leaving it somewhere in Iowa. Thereafter, he slowly worked his way West, taking jobs sticking type in print shops and small newspapers and alternating this with periods in wagon shops where he learned to handle tools.

His wanderings finally brought him to San Francisco, where he signed on as cook's helper in a windjammer. He remembers it as a six-masted schooner with a load of lumber. The ship called at various South American ports where it took on such cargoes as green hides and copra, two highly aromatic items. Rounding the Horn it delivered its shipments at various Atlantic ports.

Dick went to sea more than once during his formative years, and chance bits of conversation suggest that he was on speaking terms with ports in all parts of the world before he was nineteen. In casual conversation he often spins yarns about odd characters in strange places, like the derelict in Antofagasta, Chile, who gave him the following distinction between a "white man and a beachcomber":

"A white man develops a taste for white women and brown liquor. A beachcomber is color-blind."

In those years of wandering and working over a large part of the world, Dilworth had no predisposition toward mechanics that he can remember. He became a machinist because it was a way for a teen-ager to earn a living. In order to get jobs, he frequently told the foreman that he knew more than he did, then proceeded to make up for his deficiency by quick wit, observation, and an ability to make friends with older people who would take the kid aside and show him things.

He picked up the beginnings of an electrical education in the same way. At Cory, Pennsylvania, though he knew nothing about electricity, he signed on as a telephone lineman,

and somehow got away with the job without getting electro-
cuted in the process.

To illustrate his electrical shortcomings he recalls his
baffling efforts to repair a telephone that insisted on getting
out of order. The telephone was in the upstairs hall of an
apartment over a store. When he went down to fix the telephone in the morning, the woman would open her living-
room door to warm up the hall for him. Presently the telephone would come to life and Dilworth would pack up his
kit, confident that he had fixed the phone, though not quite
sure how he had done it.

The next morning the phone would be out of order again,
and shortly after he arrived and the living-room door was
opened, it would mysteriously come to life. Dick finally discovered a wire in a slot behind the phone, and a tack driven
through the wire. When the hall cooled off at night, the
wire would contract, pulling away from its moorings and
forming a disconnect. When the hall warmed up, the wire
expanded and pushed back into place, restoring the connection. Since it took Dick a week or more to discover this simple
phenomenon, he concludes that his electrical knowledge at
that time was almost nil.

Dick soon tired of his telephone job, and when he had a
chance to take a trip with pay, he leaped at it. The man who
was to have such a profound influence on the railroads of his
country had already traveled the railroads considerably, but
he had never paid a fare. He had gained his first intimate
knowledge of railroading from the vantage point of open
boxcars or, if boxcar doors were locked, the rods. Now there
came to him the chance to take an authorized trip on a rail-

road with pay, and the idea was novel. A logging locomotive known as the Climax was manufactured in Cory, and Dilworth was invited to escort it to Astoria, Oregon, the same town in which his father and Si Lotus Jones had warred against the crimps.

Nothing about this trip gave him any leanings toward railroading. The logging locomotive was a stubby workhorse capable of perhaps ten miles an hour. The drive shaft was disconnected, and the locomotive was taken West in a freight train. Dick lived and slept in it, oiled it once in a while, and enjoyed the scenery.

For Dilworth, those were carefree and irresponsible days, and the turning points that were to prepare him for a brilliant career as a locomotive designer were extremely haphazard. At the time he had no idea what he wanted to do.

Returning from Astoria, Dick went to work for the Westinghouse Machine Company in Pittsburgh, learned to use a machinist's manual and a slide rule, and stayed put until the spring weather got into his blood.

"I woke up one morning, and there was a bird on the windowsill," he recalls. "So a couple of us got a skiff and started to float down the Ohio River."

That was the life! Money in the pocket, a breeze in the face, and a current to carry you along. Huck Finn on his raft could hardly have been happier—until a tow of coal barges ran the boat down and wrecked it. The two boys swam ashore, hopped a freight train, and rode in style to Charleston, West Virginia, where they were routed out of their boxcar and booted out of the yards by the head-end shack (brakeman).

"Whenever I got kicked off a train, I made a practice of

working for a while in that town before I moved on. If I just got chased off, it was another matter, but being kicked off is injurious to a man's self-respect. He's got to work a while so he can get a straight neck once more."

He got a job in Charlie Ward's boiler shop, straightened his neck, faced the world with his head up, and enjoyed life as only a nineteen-year-old can. It was in Charleston that a combination of corn liquor and companionship provided the next important step toward an engineering career.

His companions at the time were some fellow workmen at the boiler shop, a couple of Kanoya (Kanawha) River steamboat men, and several men who were operating a Boer War tent show. One of them, a Paul Kruger, claimed to be a nephew of Oom Paul Kruger, the famous Boer patriot.

There was a Navy recruiting office in town at that time. Dilworth had no intention of visiting it until a long session of companionship and conviviality made him restless.

From corn likker to Navy

"Trouble was, those fellows could drink that white corn likker better than I could," he confesses. "I was out of my class and didn't know it. Warped my judgment. So I went down to the recruiting office and enlisted. I tried to ship as a machinist, but I was too skinny. So I went outside, lied a little off my age to justify my lack of heft, and went back and shipped as a landsman, with the idea that I could pick up the machinist job after I got in.

"Then, when I was in, I discovered that a machinist had to work. There was another job in the Navy that seemed to be easier, the job of electrician. So I became an electrician."

The formalities by which Dilworth became an electrician third class, U.S.N., were extremely simple. They had nothing to do with electricity. He was sent to the Navy "baby farm," the training station at Newport, Rhode Island. It was there he discovered that machinists had to work, and therefore it might be wiser to become an electrician. He put in his application and was told to go down to the power house.

There he found the chief electrician sitting in an armchair, half asleep. The old-timer looked the youngster over, removed a pipe from his mouth, and asked: "Can you start a steam engine?"

It happened that Dick could. He had learned how at the Westinghouse Machine Company, which made Corliss steam engines. So he answered yes. That was his entire electrical examination for the Navy.

Before he had been in the service long, he met a brawny electrician who had three mysterious letters tattooed on the back of his hand, spaced about an inch apart. The letters were E, I, and R. Dick asked what they meant.

"The E stands for voltage," the man answered, "the I for current and the R for resistance. They're what you use when you're figgerin' Ohm's law."

The curious youngster wanted to know more.

"Well, if you want to know the value of one of them things, you cover it with your thumb. Then you either multiply or divide the other two, and you've got it. Like for instance," he went on, "suppose you want E—that's voltage. You cover the E with your finger and multiply I times R and there's your voltage. If you want to find *R*—resistance—you cover up the *R* and divide *E* by *I*."

Thus Dilworth's introduction to the mathematics of electricity was a set of tattoo marks on the back of a sailor's hand.

Dilworth never studied anything that he had no immediate use for. Up to now, the sum total of his electrical experience had been shooting telephone trouble and hooking up doorbells. In the Navy, faced with an array of electrical equipment, he turned to "book larnin' " with a vengeance. The battleship *Kearsarge*, on which he served during the latter part of his enlistment, had seven steam-driven generators, motors on turrets, motors on the ammunition hoists and the ventilating system. There was an electrical intercommunication system and fire-control apparatus.

The turret-turning device on the *Kearsarge* was of special interest. It had a kind of control then fairly new, called the Ward-Leonard. In this system, an engine-driven generator is connected to a single motor which swings the turret. The control of the direction and speed of swing is accomplished by varying the field strength both of the generator and of the motor. Dilworth's familiarity with this kind of control was later to take him into the development of the gas-electric rail car, the immediate ancestor of the Diesel locomotive.

Dilworth gained a thorough practical knowledge of electricity in the Navy. He was discharged in May, 1909, as a chief electrician. Gradually, without knowing it, he was fitting himself to become the leading locomotive designer of his time.

Chapter 2

THE GAS-ELECTRIC
RAIL CAR

At the age of twenty-four Dilworth was becoming a good all-around machinist and electrician, but he had yet to find a job that challenged him. He went to work for the Philadelphia branch of the Stoddard-Dayton Company, makers of automobiles that were considered among the finest of their day. He stayed at this for something less than a year. One day he attempted to crank a car. The crank spun the other way, hit his wrist, and knocked the bones out through the skin. He bears the scar to this day.

When his arm was healed, he got a job with the General Electric Company at Schenectady as a machinist attached to the outside construction force. He worked on the first big dam of the Susquehanna River, the McCall's Ferry dam. Then came the break that was to determine his career and engrave

his name for all time in the annals of rail transportation in
this country.

In July of that year—1910—General Electric began search-
ing its records for men with special skills who might be useful
in handling gas-electric rail cars. They stumbled on Dilworth
as a part machinist and part electrician, a man who knew
something about the Ward-Leonard control, a fiddle-footed
bachelor who could be sent anywhere. Dilworth was called
to Schenectady for development work.

At Schenectady, Dilworth discovered that a rail car was a
passenger and baggage car powered by an eight-cylinder V-
type gasoline engine driving a generator, which in turn drove
traction motors on the axles. This was internal combustion
on rails. It wasn't the first instance of a gasoline engine being
used to drive a railroad car, but it was all new to Dilworth.

At that time, interurban lines were common throughout
the country, but the cars in interurban service were simply
streetcars running between towns. They got their power from
a third rail or an overhead trolley. The rail car being built at
Schenectady made its own electricity as it went along.

The idea appealed to Dilworth. It was new and revolutionary. And it contained elements familiar to him. He understood gasoline engines, and he knew generators and motors.

"Right there," he says, "I swore a horrible oath that I was
going to stay with that kind of motive power until it was
pulling the *Twentieth Century Limited*, which was at that
time a rather new but well-known train running through
Schenectady."

As it turned out, his dream was to come true. He stayed with
it through the years, as long as anybody would pay wages.

There were periods when there was no money for development, and at those times Dilworth worked on something else, but the moment internal-combustion rail cars were revived he returned to his first love—the first genuine enthusiasm of his errant career.

When Dilworth reported to Schenectady, development work on the rail car was about five years along. One demonstration car was out on the branch lines of the railroads, showing what it could do.

At Schenectady, in 1910, Dilworth met Ambrose "Jimmy" Heseltine, who was jockeying the demonstrator. Like Dilworth, Heseltine was to remain with this new kind of motive power until it was hauling most of the passenger and freight trains of the nation.

The day they met, when Dilworth was out of the shop on some errand, Heseltine glanced curiously into the tool kit of the young ex-Navy machinist and electrician.

"A good machinist," Heseltine says, "usually showed up with an impressive tool kit. Dilworth's contained a hammer, a screwdriver, a slab of chewing tobacco, and a 25-foot coil of light rope."

When confronted with this incident, Dilworth grunts noncommittally.

"I don't know where I accumulated that many tools," he replies. "In those days, the traditional boomer's kit consisted of a 6-inch scale and a pair of outside calipers, carried in his pocket."

Working on rail cars, Dilworth changed from a boomer mechanic to a man with a mission in life. In the busy years from 1910 to 1914, General Electric built and sold some eighty-five rail cars, and these were glorious days for the young engineer.

His first job was to help develop an engine for the cars. In 1910 there wasn't a gasoline engine made in the United States powerful enough to generate electricity for the rail car. The first two G.E. demonstrators had imported engines. The engine under development at Schenectady had the same kind of valve gearing as the Stoddard-Dayton engine; so Dilworth was able to make some contributions to the design.

While working on the engine, Dilworth decided to improve his background by signing up for a correspondence course in automobile engines. His first lesson came and proved to be general in content. The second lesson contained a breakdown of "the most modern automobile engine." It proved to be the engine of the 1905 Oldsmobile, a design that was out of date by 5 years. Dilworth threw the course into the waste-basket. Most of his life was to be spent doing what he was doing then—working on experimental designs far ahead of anything in the current textbooks.

Early in 1911, a rail car with the new engine passed its tests and was delivered to the Southern Railway with Heseltine as the jockey and Dilworth as his assistant. They traveled the Southern states together, teaching steam engineers the art of handling internal combustion and electricity.

Now Dilworth's education took a new turn. As an engineer operating a power car on the railroad network, he had to learn railroad operation. He bought and avidly devoured every technical railroad magazine he could find. By reading, talking, and observation, he learned the operational side of railroading from track ballast to water tower.

After breaking in under Heseltine, Dilworth delivered cars on his own, and as production increased and the crew of jockeys multiplied in all parts of the country, it became necessary to appoint supervisors to ride herd on the jockeys. In 1911, Dilworth was made road foreman of jockeys over a wide territory extending from St. Paul to Mexico.

Keeping the wayward jockeys in line, servicing the cars, and making the railroad men happy was strenuous business, and after about a year of it, the young engineer began to tire of small hotels and boardinghouses. He wanted to get married and settle down; so he applied for and received a transfer to Erie to help develop experimental cars.

As a record of his days beyond the Mississippi supervising jockeys, he has memorized word for word one dubious testimonial on the value of his services to General Electric. It was written by his successor. This man, after spending two weeks following Dilworth's tracks over the plains, wrote the following report to the home office:

"I have been carefully over Mr. Dilworth's territory, and as nearly as I can find out the only thing Mr. Dilworth ever did in this territory was to drink whisky and shoot craps."

To this criticism, Dilworth enters the mild explanation that it was a whisky-drinking, crapshooting job, but that wasn't *all* he did. To this, another early rail-car man, Jimmy Hilton, heartily agrees.

Like Dilworth, Jimmy Hilton was to become one of the small band of pioneers who ushered in the era of the Diesel locomotive. In 1912, Hilton was in charge of a small fleet of gas-electric cars bought by the Frisco Lines. He bore the impressive title of General Inspector of Motor Cars, but he insists that he was not only inspector, but repairman and laborer as well, since there wasn't a man in the shops who knew how to fix a gas-electric. One boiling hot day in August he brought one of the Bull Moose cars—so named because 1912 was the year in which Teddy Roosevelt bolted the Republican party and organized the Bull Moosers—into Lawton, Oklahoma. The car was limping along on one traction motor.

Dick Dilworth was in Lawton, and together the two men, working in 110-degree temperature, jacked up the front end of the car, wheeled out the front truck, and went to work on the motor connections. They went uptown, got some sections of brass pipe and a blowtorch, and managed to solder together a cable. Then they took the two magneto armatures into town and located a foot lathe. With Hilton working the pedals, Dilworth turned down the face of the collector rings in order to take the skip and bang out of the magnetos. After that, they reassembled the car.

"Dick was never one to duck his share of the dirty work," Hilton concluded. "Here at La Grange, whenever we had trouble in the test department on those first streamliners, Dick would come down himself, instead of taking somebody else's report. As far as I can see, he has never gotten out of the habit of taking off his coat and going to work, the way he did that day in Lawton."

This willingness to get dirty on the job was one reason why the Dilworth of 1912 cut a somewhat carefree and disreputable appearance as he traveled the country servicing gas-electrics. Out of this fact arose a humbling experience that he likes to recall whenever his sense of importance begins to swell out of proportion.

It happened in Matamoros, Mexico, where he had gone to service a rail car. After exploring the car's innards and correcting its ailments, he made his way to a *tiendo* for a glass of beer. At that moment five tough-looking *ladrones* came in and proceeded to stick up the joint.

The first thought that crossed Dick's mind was that Americans weren't very popular just then. A local revolt against the Madero government was under way, and the revolutionaries were inclined to blame not only Madero but the United States for most of their ills. Dilworth was certain that he would be spotted as an American and singled out for some special treatment.

"In those days my stomach curved inward instead of outward, and when one of the *ladrones* stuck his gun at my belt, my stomach rubbed my backbone."

With the bandit's first words, however, Dick experienced a great letdown.

"*Al otro lado, gringo*," the man said gruffly. "*No queremos a usted.*"

Roughly translated, this means: "Other side, white guy. We don't want you."

"They took one look at me," Dilworth reflects, "and decided that I wasn't even worth robbing."

To this day, Dilworth uses this incident as a club, to bat down his own ego.

Sidetracked

In 1912, Dilworth forsook the road and settled down to family life in Erie. On February 20, he married Ada Ed-

wards, a Bryn Mawr girl whom he had met while working at
the Stoddard-Dayton plant in Philadelphia, in 1909. The first
of their family of four children, Richard Edwards, was born
in Erie and today helps make locomotives in La Grange.

Dilworth remained at Erie for about a year, working on
test cars, after which General Electric's interest in rail cars
began to wane.

There were various reasons for this, chief of which was that
the company was more interested in pushing the electrifica-
tion of railroads. The Chicago, Milwaukee and St. Paul had
recently been electrified, and to G.E. this seemed the way of
the future. Another reason was the company's difficulty in
teaching the rail-car art to railroad men. Operating the cars
called for certain skills that steam engineers had trouble mas-
tering. As long as G.E. jockeys remained with the cars to
preside over the mysteries of gas engines and electrical equipment, the cars ran well. But when the factory representatives
departed, the troubles began. From 1913, when interest in
the gas-electrics tapered off, to 1918, most of the eighty-five
cars sold to the railroads were set aside and painted in white
lead. Cars that had sold for $28,000 to $38,000 were offered
at $3,000, with no takers.

As a result, Dilworth was separated from his first love by
the fact that nobody would pay him money to work on it. In
1913 he went to work on an experimental Diesel-engine development G.E. was undertaking at the time. The company
was building a variety of Diesels, most of them two-cycle air-
injection engines with opposed pistons. Dilworth had charge
of construction and test.

Diesel development

At that time, nobody in the United States knew much about Diesels. These remarkable engines that burned oil and needed no spark plugs were a European development. As Dilworth explains the beginnings of G.E.'s experimental work:

"We bought a Swedish Diesel and a French one, set 'em up on the test floor and ran 'em. Then we practiced taking 'em apart and putting 'em together, and part of the time we got 'em together right. Anyhow, we got a little bit acquainted with them."

While they were practicing on the French and Swedish Diesels, they were also developing their own opposed-piston design. As experimental-floor foreman in charge of this work, Dilworth was again driven to book learning with a vengeance. At the ripe age of twenty-seven, Dick was older than most of the cub engineers who were doing the design work, and when he didn't like what they were doing, he had to seek arguments to support his views, and that meant considerable boning in books, late at night.

Dilworth found, for example, that the lubrication system laid out by the designers failed to get the oil to the wrist pin. Dick searched every book he could find on the subject of hydraulic rams, which had nothing to do with Diesel engines but had much to do with the inertia of a fluid in a pipe. Eventually he found the answer and corrected the trouble.

"My job, as floor foreman," he says, "was to get the oil to the place where it should be, not on paper but in the machine itself."

As Dilworth helped to shape the design of these first Diesels, he may have thought that he was being sidetracked from his dream of putting gas-electric cars to work pulling the country's trains. Actually, the work was an important step in his training for the job of Dieselizing American railroads. He couldn't have imagined it then, but just 20 years later, a new and improved Diesel engine was to replace the gasoline engine as the prime mover that would generate electricity for the first streamliners, and Dilworth was to have the job of designing and installing the power cars. As experimental-floor foreman in 1912–1913, he was being fitted for the role of man of the hour in the early 1930s.

Dilworth's education as a resourceful engineer made rapid strides in these days. He learned something from books but even more from the demands of the job and from his associates. He was working closely at this time with Dr. Herman Lemp, an electrical genius in the class of Steinmetz and Pupin, a man who had worked earlier in the laboratory of Thomas Edison. Lemp was one of the senior engineers in charge of Diesel development for G.E.

"I learned a lot from Lemp," Dilworth recalls. "Lemp always worked from the positive side. When a problem came up that seemed insoluble, Lemp would look around and see what we had to work with. Instead of looking for the difficulties, he'd take an inventory of the favorable factors, and go on from there. If one way wouldn't work, he'd try another. He was one of those men who literally never gave up."

Dilworth also absorbed another quality from Lemp—an ability to recognize the similarity of problems.

"Maybe something happened years ago," Dilworth explains,

"when Lemp was trying to develop the first X-ray machines. Later on, if that same thing happened when he was trying to build a Diesel, he'd recognize it, even though the circumstances were entirely different. Lemp looked way below the surface of things. He'd recognize a basic idea wherever he saw it, and he'd remember what happened to it the first time. I think I had the same faculty to a lesser extent."

In 1914, Dilworth took some of the G.E. Diesels to the Philippines and installed them in Fort Drum, the "concrete battleship" at the mouth of Manila Bay. Mrs. Dilworth went with him to discover in due course that the lot of an engineer's wife contains an element of adventure. Three times, her Manila house was wrecked by hurricanes. Their second child, Margaret J., was born in the Hospice San Pablo in the old walled city of Manila. Many years later, the first Japanese bomb to fall on Manila was to level this hospital.

When Dilworth was finished with his task of installing Diesels, he served for a time as civilian engineer for the Engineering Corps, and in 1918 returned to Erie, Pennsylvania.

By that time G.E. had ceased almost all development either on rail cars or on Diesel engines; so Dilworth was assigned to steam turbines and marine reduction gears. While at work on this project he engaged in a study that revealed how thorough his engineering background had become, without benefit of college training. He was assigned the task of finding the error in an engineering formula. As he explains it, somewhat reluctantly:

"During the first war, a German did a considerable amount of research on the dynamic balancing of rotating masses. He wanted to cash in on it in this country, but Germans were unpopular over here; so he sent a Russian to front for him, and he actually sold four copies of the formula at $30,000 a copy. G.E. was one of the suckers.

"They were entirely dissatisfied with the formula. However, it did appear to point out that there was a way to figure dynamic balance that would make the balancing of rotating machinery much cheaper. So they set several people to working on it. One was an excellent mathematician.

"I was another one, probably because I had already done something on the static balance of thin disks. The mathematician was able to leap from crag to crag in his study, whereas I—not having had the benefit of higher mathematics—had to wallow through all the hills and valleys and explore the blind canyons, using simple arithmetic, geometry, and trigonometry. It just happened that a very good answer lay in one of those blind canyons that the higher mathematician didn't have to explore.

"What happened was that because of my lack of higher mathematics I had to make many more layouts. Some of the layouts wouldn't lie quiet on the paper; so I had to put parallel planes on the drawing board, sticking knitting needles through them to get into the third dimension—and that's where the answer was."

Dilworth puffs on his pipe a moment.

"If all that sounds a bit complicated, you might put it this way: because I had to take an elementary approach, I found an answer that the educated man missed."

The incident provides a clue to the development of a brilliant analytical mind. Perhaps because he is self-educated, Dilworth has refused to be trapped by the complications of higher mathematics. Whenever he is confronted by involved ideas, his first attack is to reduce them to simple terms. He believes in higher mathematics, but only as a tool to prove or disprove ideas that are basically simple.

Dilworth's discovery of the right formula for the balancing of rotating masses resulted in great savings in the building of such things as turbine rotors. This ability of his to find the right answers was to show up later in a series of brilliantly conceived formulas to predict the behavior of Diesel locomotives.

Dilworth stayed with steam turbines from 1918 into the first years of the roaring twenties, at which time the railroads began to show a renewed interest in gas-electric rail cars.

Back on the track

By 1923, many of the old G.E. cars were going back into service (some are still operating) and a number of companies were beginning to manufacture their own versions of the gas-electric, among them a Cleveland company headed by H. L. Hamilton called the Electro-Motive Engineering Corporation.

Dick explains the revival of the rail car this way. First of all, the need was greater than ever. Rail cars were used on the branch lines as cost reducers, since they could be operated for a fraction of the cost of even a small steam train. With the rising competition of busses and trucks, branch lines were losing money faster than ever, and the need for economy was correspondingly greater. The railroads had come out of World

War I in sad condition, and many branch lines were in an advanced state of decrepitude.

Even more important, in Dilworth's opinion, was the fact that during the years from 1914 to 1920 the nation was flooded with low-cost automobiles. The youth of the land was flivver-conscious. Gasoline alley had appeared on the American scene, and if there was a boy in the family, it was a sure bet that he could take down and put together a car. This new generation, filtering into the mechanical departments of the railroads, wasn't in the least awed by a piece of rolling stock powered by a gasoline engine that in turn ran a generator. Old steam men might be repelled, but not the new crop of flivver fixers. So rail cars in 1923 entered upon a renewed career of popularity.

Dilworth got himself transferred back to what was left of G.E.'s gas-electric department and began contacting the various companies building cars. Of these the most promising was the Electro-Motive company of Hal Hamilton.

Hamilton was building a 57-foot car powered by a 175-horsepower Winton gasoline engine, and Dilworth liked what he saw. Most of the other budding rail-car companies were trying to put automobile trucks and busses on rails, and Dilworth saw little future in any such compromise. Hamilton, on the other hand, had taken up where General Electric had left off, adding all the advancement in engines, electricity, and car construction that had taken place in the interval. Of them all, Dick decided that Hamilton knew where he was going.

For about a year and a half Dick was contact man between General Electric and Electro-Motive, acting as consultant on all matters electrical. Then, on January 1, 1926, Hamilton took him on as chief engineer of the growing company. By this time a number of the old gas-electric men had flocked to the Hamilton standard, among them Jimmy Hilton, Ambrose Heseltine, and Ernie Kuehn, a big six-footer who had supervised gas-electrics for the Cotton Belt Railroad in the old days.

Dilworth recalls his first meeting with Hamilton. He was taken in to meet the president of the new company by Bill Leggett, Cleveland representative of G.E.

"I was very much impressed with Hamilton, but he wasn't impressed with me," Dilworth remembers. "He said later that I neither looked nor talked like an engineer and he doubted that I had any very clear conception of his problems."

Dilworth didn't know it, but he had already become something of a legend in rail-car circles. His reputation had preceded him, and Hamilton knew exactly what he was doing when he hired Dilworth for his chief engineer.

"Wear a nightshirt"

One story about Dilworth in particular had impressed Hamilton—a story that engineers and railroad men took great relish in telling over their coffee cups.

It happened when Dilworth was supervising the installing of electrical equipment on a rail car on which an engineer employed by the car builder was responsible for the engine. We'll call this man Smith.

When Dick saw the drawings, he didn't like the coupling between the generator and the engine. It was too solid. Without play or flexibility, something would have to give. He called this to Smith's attention, and the man in effect told him to mind his own business, that Dilworth could take care of the electrical equipment and he'd take care of the engine.

Dilworth rolled up his plans and prepared to leave the man's office, whereupon Smith asked what he was going to do about it.

"I'm going back and put a larger shaft in the generator," Dick replied. "If anything busts, it won't be the generator."

Smith told him to go ahead. Before departing Dilworth borrowed a sheet of paper and drew a little sketch on which he indicated a crankshaft failure at the second throw. He sealed this in an envelope and marked on the outside, "Open next July 4."

Dilworth had done some fast figuring in Smith's office. From what he knew of stresses and strains and the fatigue of metal, he had figured how many revolutions of the crankshaft would bring about a failure. He also was able to figure how many crankshaft revolutions would occur in a normal day's operation of the rail car. Assuming that the rail car would operate the average number of days per month, he had been able to arrive at the conclusion that the overstressed crankshaft would fail on or about the following July 4.

Apparently he was wrong, for shortly after the following July 4 he received a letter from Smith stating that the rail car was still in operation and doing well. The letter was full of triumph and abuse.

"It should have been written on asbestos paper," Dick recalls. "It reported that the coupling was standing up, and as a prophet I was a fake."

Just a month later, Dick got word from a third party that

the engine's crankshaft had broken. He asked the man if the rail car had been operating continuously throughout the year, and learned something greatly to his satisfaction. The man told him that for one month it had been laid up for repairs having nothing to do with the crankshaft. If it had operated normally, it would have broken on or about July 4, exactly as Dilworth had predicted.

Dick met Smith and a representative of the car-building company in a hotel lobby in Philipsburg, Pennsylvania. The lobby was crowded, but Smith, ignoring the strangers, was storming. Far from admitting his error, he was apparently trying to lay the blame on the generator. His technique was to let loose a sheer torrent of abuse.

The third man present suggested that they go into a private dining room, for fear the language might have a bad effect on the hotel's patrons. When they reached this room, Dick realized that logic or argument would have little effect; so he adopted a stratagem he had often used throughout his career. He said:

"Before we go into this, I want to tell a little story."

Smith sputtered but reluctantly subsided.

"During the San Francisco earthquake," Dick began, "out in the residential district, the side of a house fell out and a bed slid into the street. A man and his wife were in the bed. The wife, dressed in a nightgown, got out of one side of the bed and looked down at her husband who lay there with the covers pulled up to his chin. She said to him: 'Maybe this will teach you not to go to bed without a nightshirt.' "

Dilworth didn't need to point out that Smith had been caught bare and defenseless in a public place. The implication was plain, and from that point on, negotiations proceeded in a more sweetly reasonable atmosphere.

It was this tale, the story of a remarkable bit of prophecy and a blunt way of doing business, that had preceded Dilworth to Electro-Motive and had convinced Hamilton that Dilworth was the man for the job.

As the two men worked together, Hamilton discovered in Dilworth a man who was more interested in the rail car itself than he was in selling something, and this pleased the head of Electro-Motive. During those days, Hamilton was approached by many electrical representatives, each one interested in getting Hamilton to adopt the specialty he was selling. Of them all, only Dilworth seemed to put the rail car first.

Thus on January 1, 1926, Dilworth entered upon a quarter century of service during which time he was to have active charge of the design of gas-electrics, then of Diesel locomotives. From the first, he was besieged by people trying to sell him something, but Dilworth steadfastly refused to be bewitched by gadgets.

For several years he carried on a running fight with the electrical suppliers who were forever trying to complicate the product, whereas Dilworth was bent on keeping it simple. The undercover battle became particularly sanguine in the case of electrical controls, specifically those controls designed to prevent the operator from what might be called (in automobile terms) stalling or racing the engine.

This struggle came to a head in a meeting of the Association of American Railroads at Atlantic City in 1930, when the representative of a large electrical company delivered an excellent paper, during which the speaker said that rail cars could be much improved if the engineers of rail-car companies would allow the electrical engineer more freedom.

Dilworth knew that the jab was aimed at him. After the paper was finished, he rose, complimented the speaker, and said: "I think he's talking about me. At any rate, the shoe fits, so I'll put it on. He is referring to the differential field control as compared with the torque control, as it is sometimes called. I have examined some two or three thousand methods of control. The patent office is full of them. There's not too much difference between them. I suspect that, if we were to install the best of them in one rail car and the worst in another, there wouldn't be three-tenths of 1 per cent difference in the operation of the car."

This ended all talk of controls for many years and at the same time reaffirmed Dilworth's stand that the excellence of the gadget itself was unimportant. The only question to be answered was, how did it affect the operation of the rail car— or locomotive?

During the next five or six years, Electro-Motive built some five hundred rail cars, or more than three-fourths of all rail cars built during that period.

In the first cars the power unit, consisting of engine and electrical equipment, occupied a small space at the head end of the car with the balance devoted to baggage and passengers. The car was of light construction, weighing about thirty-five tons, and was intended as a fast, economical passenger and express service on branch lines.

The railroads soon discovered that the rail car was an effective tool in reducing branch-line costs. Even more important, the car drew patronage. People liked the fast schedules, the smooth ride, and the absence of soot and cinders.

Because rail cars were a success, they were inadequate almost from the beginning. More people wanted to ride them than could be accommodated, and the only cure for this was to build more powerful engines in order to haul a second and third coach behind the first.

So the railroads demanded more power. The Winton engines used in Electro-Motive cars went from the original 175 horsepower to 220, 275, 300, and 400. Electro-Motive even delivered some cars containing two engines totaling 800 horsepower.

It was almost inevitable that these heavier and more powerful cars should be used for any job at hand. Railroads began using them to pull short trains, to haul freight, and even to serve as switchers. Without quite knowing it, the railroads at this time were making their first serious attempt to break the century-old monopoly of steam. They were discovering the merits of a power car that was available most of the day or night and needed no boiler water.

The distillate burner

The railroads kept asking for power, but unfortunately Electro-Motive had just about reached a ceiling. It was not only difficult to crowd more than 800 horsepower into a car, but the cost of gasoline was rising to a point where the rail car's margin of economy was disappearing. To avoid this dilemma, Hamilton went hunting for a power plant burning cheaper fuel. He asked Dilworth to work with the Winton Engine Company on an engine that would burn distillates at three cents a gallon instead of gasoline at fifteen.

Dilworth remembers with a wry grimace the 5-year struggle to create a distillate burner. He doesn't consider the campaign a success, though out of it arose certain benefits that have been of permanent value to the railroad business.

First of all, Dilworth had to discover what a distillate was. About the best definition he could arrive at was that it was anything that didn't classify as heavy fuel oil. It might range from a low-grade gasoline, to painter's naphtha, to gas oil. In fact it was anything the refinery didn't happen to want at that particular time.

The most uniform product Dilworth came across was something known as Dubbs oil, the heavy half of the pressure benzine taken off during the Dubbs cracking process. Attempting to burn this stuff in a carburetor engine, according to Dilworth, was grim business.

"In order to mix Dubbs oil with air and get it safely into the cylinder, we had to have a carburetor on each pair of cylinders," Dilworth recalls, "and these carburetors were fearful and wonderful things. On our largest model we even converted the intake valve of each cylinder into a carburetor, so that the mixture could be introduced into the cylinder practically at once."

Burning the stuff after it got into the cylinder was like "trying to set fire to a wet haystack." The designers had to put four spark plugs in each cylinder head. Where a gasoline engine would fire with one spark plug carrying about 35 milliamperes at 10,000 volts, the four spark plugs of the distillate engine each delivered 70 milliamperes at 20,000 volts.

A number of distillate burners were produced, climaxed by a twelve-cylinder V-engine with a 9-inch bore and 12-inch stroke. It was a heavy and somewhat clumsy engine weighing about 35,000 pounds and rated at 900 horsepower. It was installed on a Santa Fe train and was still running in 1950, though most of its life it burned gasoline instead of Dubbs oil. This happened because in the early years of the depression, when the engine was put into service, the price of gasoline dropped.

Though the entire distillate experiment was a kind of comedy of errors and compromises, some by-product advantages occurred when the big engine was installed in its power car, and this story furnishes an interesting side light on the way engineering developments happen.

The engine and generator for this job were so heavy that it took two trucks and a special body to carry them. So the railroad planned a power body 22 feet long, this body to be articulated to a 60-foot baggage car.

Up to this time, common railroad practice called for attaching the brake cylinder to the bottom of the car. However, on the distillate power car it was also necessary to have the fuel tank attached to the bottom. When it came to putting both fuel tank and brake cylinders on the bottom of the 22-foot power unit, there simply wasn't room.

So Dilworth conceived the idea that the large brake cylinder should be broken up into small cylinders and "draped around the truck as close as possible to the brake shoes on the driving wheels."

Dilworth, Hamilton, and Kuehn had discussed this before, but the idea was so shockingly new and irregular that there had been no chance to put their dreams to the test. What gave them their chance was articulation.

Articulation wasn't new. Articulation simply meant that one truck carried the tail end of one car and the front end of another. This eliminated one truck entirely and permitted two cars to be closely coupled. It really converted two cars into a single car that could conveniently bend in the middle. It had been tried in Canada on a train and in this country on street-cars. But Canada had tried articulation only on cars back somewhere in the train. They had never tried it on the power car, and railroad men were afraid of what would happen to an articulated power-and-baggage car at high speed. Would it jackknife, leap from the rails, or buckle? Its use in streetcar service was no test, since streetcars were slow.

Rather than take the responsibility of ordering the articu-lated power unit, Santa Fe threw the burden on Electro-Mo-tive. Electro-Motive had not only to order the car but to guarantee it.

This set Dilworth free to do what he wanted about the brake cylinder; so he took the big cylinder off the bottom of the car, broke it up into smaller cylinders, and "draped them around."

The railroads predicted dire calamity. One well-known au-thority said that this crazy power-and-baggage unit wouldn't run 50 miles without turning over in a ditch. Another said simply that it was "manslaughter."

They objected to the lack of the stiffening action of the

brake rigging between truck and car body. They objected to
the use of an air pipe as an equalizer between brake shoes.
With great misgivings they put the car into service—and
nothing happened.

Today, putting the brake cylinders on the trucks is accepted
practice on almost all passenger cars and locomotives. But
hardly anyone remembers that the brake cylinders were moved
down to the trucks simply because there wasn't room for both
brake cylinder and fuel tank on a stubby power unit built for
the Santa Fe back in 1931.

As for articulation, the power-and-baggage car ran sweetly
and in fine balance at high speed, while the rest of the train
swayed and bounced. So well did the articulated cars behave
over good and bad track that the lessons learned here were
responsible for the articulated streamliners that were soon to
appear in the form of the Union Pacific *City* trains and the
Burlington *Zephyrs*.

The railroads speed up

Those small articulated streamliners were important
in ushering in the era of the Diesel locomotive for two reasons: first, they marked the end of the gasoline and distillate
prime movers and introduced the Diesel; and second, they
were built purposely for main-line service. That 900-horse-
power distillate of the Santa Fe marks the end of a story—
the story of the rail car on the branch line.

It is well to remember at this point that whether we men-
tion the rail car, the Streamliners, or the later Diesel locomo-

tives, we are talking about the same thing. All of them have engines that generate electricity, which is then used to turn the wheels. The only differences are those of size, complication, and function. The Diesel locomotive was really born when the rail cars were proved a success. Only nobody knew it.

What brought awareness was the growing appetite of the railroads for speed. In the early years of the depression, the railroads were losing patronage to slim pocketbooks, to the highways, and to the airplane. For what business was left, the competition grew stern.

The roads tried various lures, chief among which was sumptuous meals. The outstanding example was the competition of the Burlington, Milwaukee, and North Western between Chicago and St. Paul–Minneapolis. Starting from Chicago just before dinner, they lured passengers with a ten-course meal for a dollar. For a while this bait was effective. But after a time the lure faded and the passenger total failed materially to increase.

In a sort of probing, or cut-and-try process, the railroads proceeded over a period of years to develop speed and high regularity of service as passenger attractions.

The Union Pacific was strong for rail cars—they had many on their branch lines. So when they went for speed, they decided to put the rail car on the main line in the form of a small three-car articulated train. They dreamed up a lightweight aluminum train, powered with a 600-horsepower gasoline engine. This train, the *City of Salina*, with its shining sides and its modern interior decorations, attracted tremendous newspaper space before it ever ran a mile.

The Burlington lost no time coming along with its version of speed on the main line. It was also a small articulated train known as the *Pioneer Zephyr*, but it was made of stainless steel, and it was to have the honor of being the first successful main-line train powered by a Diesel engine.

Thus it was speed that brought internal combustion to the main line. And it was the Diesel engine, first used on the *Zephyr*, that lifted the horsepower ceiling and made possible the big locomotives of today.

In 1934, when the era of the rail car was to be succeeded by the age of small, fast streamlined trains, Dick Dilworth was forty-nine years old.

He had already achieved as much as most well-known engineers achieve in a lifetime; yet in a sense everything that had happened was merely training for the bigger job to come.

Beginning in 1910 he had helped put together G.E.'s early rail cars.

While jockeying these cars around the country, he had learned railroading as only a railroad man knows it.

He had helped develop the first experimental Diesel engines made in the United States, contributing many details to their successful operation.

As chief engineer for Electro-Motive, he had steered the design development of the gas-electric rail car to its peak of usefulness on the railroads, making them bigger year by year until they began to function as all-purpose locomotives.

He had built a distillate-burning engine, the most powerful internal-combustion engine used on railroads up to that time.

He had contributed to the railroad art by taking the brake

cylinder off the bottom of the railroad car and breaking it up into smaller cylinders closer to the wheels.

The foot-loose youngster who had traveled the world "stealing the trade of machinist" had gone far. But his biggest job—that of creating the first successful main-line Diesel locomotives—was still to come.

Chapter 3

THE STREAMLINERS

Back in 1910, when Dilworth was in Schenectady working on those early gas-electrics, he and a crowd of devotees used to foregather in the dining room of a compliant boardinghouse keeper on Sunday afternoons. They would set a keg of beer on the table, sit around and smoke pipes, and build Diesel locomotives.

The only trouble with their fine dreams was that the Diesel of that day was a ponderous machine. If you imagined a Diesel with enough power to pull a train, then surrounded it with the necessary plumbing and a transmission, you had a mass of machinery so heavy you couldn't get wheels under it—and so big it wouldn't go through a tunnel.

Therefore, those Sunday sessions at the boardinghouse were just dreams compounded of pipe smoke and beer froth. Now, in 1932, there was a Diesel engine compact and powerful enough to bring the dream closer to reality. It was known as the 201, and it had been developed by General Motors Research under the direction of "Boss" Kettering and the Winton Engine Company under Carl Salisbury and Ket's son Eugene Kettering.

By this time, both the Winton company and Electro-Motive had been acquired by General Motors, the Winton company on June 20, 1930, and Electro-Motive on December 31.

The 201 represented a remarkable advance in the art of Diesel-engine construction. It had been developed as a lightweight unit for Navy submarines. It was a two-cycle eight-cylinder engine, each cylinder developing 75 to 80 horsepower. The weight was only 20 pounds per horsepower, a highly efficient ratio. The frame was of welded steel, a radical departure from accepted practice, but a feature that facilitated mass production. From the service and repair standpoint, each cylinder and piston assembly was separately removable. One of the key innovations was the unit injector, by means of which solid fuel (unmixed with air) was fed into the cylinder under thousands of pounds of pressure. The advantage of the unit injector was that it eliminated the need for high pressure in long fuel lines. The pressure was created by the unit injector—which was also a pump—at the moment the fuel entered the cylinder.

Two of these engines had been installed in the General Motors exhibit at the Century of Progress Exposition in Chicago, and these were the prototypes considered by Ralph Budd, president of the Burlington Lines, for use on his *Pioneer Zephyr*.

While Budd and his assistant vice-president Fred Gurley were looking over the engines with H. L. Hamilton and Dilworth, the railroad president turned to the engineer for a frank opinion of the Diesel's merits. With his usual bluntness, he told Budd that the engine was new and untried and would run into trouble.

Budd decided to take a chance. Confident that General Motors would stand behind the engine until the bugs were ironed out, he ordered an eight-cylinder 600-horsepower 201A for the *Zephyr*, and a new kind of railroad power plant had its beginning.

The success of the Diesel-powered *Zephyr*, despite the bugs and the breakdowns, led to a kind of chain reaction. The Burlington built two more trains, the Twin City *Zephyrs*, and these competed successfully with the steam *Hiawathas* on the Chicago–Twin City run.

This in turn encouraged the Union Pacific to build more *City* trains and to power them with Diesels instead of gasoline burners.

These small streamliners, appearing early in 1934, with their silvery sides and their bright new ideas of color and furnishing, attracted overflow patronage wherever they went in service. The *City* trains cut the running time between the West Coast and Chicago from 60 hours to 40. The *Zephyr* made a memorable run from Denver to Chicago in 13 hours and 5 minutes, an average of nearly 78 miles per hour.

Inevitably longer streamliners followed, culminating in *City* trains of twelve cars powered by two Diesels delivering 2,400 horsepower and *Zephyrs* equally long with 3,000 horsepower. The Diesel was making its bow to the main line with a dramatic flourish.

Electro-Motive's share in this high-speed development,

which excited and thrilled the depression-weary United States, was to furnish the engines and the over-all layout of the power cars. Electro-Motive, in these days, had fallen away to a skeleton organization consisting of Hamilton, Dilworth, the sales manager O. F. Brookmeyer, Ernie Kuehn, Jimmy Heseltine, and a few service men scattered about the country. Dilworth's office was in the Winton Engine Company in Cleveland, and his staff consisted of a couple of draftsmen.

How to win an argument

Whenever the Union Pacific or Burlington wanted a new train, Dilworth and his two helpers would make a layout of the power car on a sheet measuring perhaps 3 feet wide by 15 feet long and would present it to a board of specialists from the railroad, the electrical companies, the car builders, as well as truckmen, air-brake men, and all the rest. As many as forty persons might be gathered around the layout to pass judgment.

Dilworth dreaded what might happen if each group of experts began to offer advice on how to improve the power car. This was a time, he decided, when it was important to man the sweep and steer the craft. If ever a budding young idea needed guidance, it was then. So he employed a stratagem.

"I played 'em a dirty trick, and to this day I don't think any of them has ever discovered it," he says, sucking on his pipe. "I'd make a practice of inserting a glaring error into the layout. I'd put it in a prominent place where it would be sure to attract everybody's attention. This would start a debate over how to correct the error, and I didn't hesitate to keep the debate going by any means at hand. Sometimes the argument lasted for 12 or 15 hours, and by that time everybody would be so exhausted that they'd adopt the balance of the layout without further talk."

It was a case of wearing down a man's capacity to disagree, and therefore of preventing the adoption of many pet ideas that had little to do with the over-all performance of the power car. It was also a case of how Dilworth kept steering the development of the Diesel locomotive in the way it wanted to go.

After a particularly harrowing session, Dick was likely to reveal the depth of his devotion to the Diesel by saying to a friend, "I'm going to put this animal where it belongs if it takes all my life."

Since these fast streamliners were new, they had their troubles, and it was up to Dilworth and his men to keep them running. At these times, Dilworth was quick to rise to the young Diesel's defense whenever a railroad man began casting aspersions.

Dilworth remembers that the winter of 1935-1936 was a particularly severe one, and this happened also to be the first winter in which the Union Pacific's *City* trains were on regular schedules. On a certain day, one of the *City* trains came in from the West Coast after a harrowing trip marred both by mechanical and weather stops. The train had run into snow, ice, and engine trouble.

"There was an inquest at which the high priest was E. B. Hall, chief mechanical officer of the North Western," Dick says. "The North Western was in on it, because the Union Pacific used their tracks from Omaha to Chicago. When we were leaving the inquest, Hall said to me: 'Dick, if you'll keep that contraption off my railroad till the weather breaks up, I'll buy you a new hat.'

"Hall was kicking my dog, and I couldn't stand for that. So I had to make a crack about his 400, the fast steam train running between Chicago and the Twin Cities. It had been having winter trouble, too, and I called this fact to his attention. Hall laughed ruefully. His only answer was: 'If you'll keep my 400 off the track until the weather breaks up, I'll buy you a new house.' Maybe I didn't win the scrap, but I figure we broke even."

But while the new Diesel-powered streamliners were having growing pains, they were showing talents hardly to be expected in a callow youth. One of these was their behavior in snow.

One day, early in the spring of that same severe winter, Budd of the Burlington realized that his *Twin Zephyrs* running between Chicago and the Twin Cities had a better on-time record during the winter months than the rival steam trains. He called in his operating vice-president and asked him how the *Zephyrs* behaved when running through snowdrifts and over snow-covered tracks. The official gave an enthusiastic report. It seemed that the Diesel, because of its heavy front end, its small wheels, and the constant smooth torque of the powered axles, had an ability to drive right through snow that would stop a steam locomotive.

Budd suggested that they get pictures, which was something of a problem, since the time was now early spring and there wasn't much snow left. The operating vice-president got around this by rounding up a crew of men to shovel snow onto the track from the fields and shaded hollows. This was done near Savannah, Illinois, on a Sunday when traffic was light.

About six feet of the soggy, wet stuff was piled onto the tracks. Cameras were set up alongside the track, and the engineer was told to hit the snow at 85 miles per hour. He made his run but lost his nerve at the last moment and hit the snow at a mere 75 miles an hour.

The resultant pictures were sensational. According to Dilworth they looked like a preview of the explosion of a hydrogen bomb, with snow flying in all directions and the train almost completely hidden. But the *Zephyr* cleared the track as neatly as if a snowplow had gone through, and kept right on going. The point was proved, and the Burlington made full use of the event in its publicity.

The Streamliners proved the ability of the Diesel locomotive to maintain fast passenger schedules on the main line. But though they made nice profits in themselves they had their faults, chief of which was that they were inflexible in their make-up. They were fixed-consist trains. A breakdown in any one car would throw the whole train out of service.

The railroads found themselves in the dilemma of having educated the public to fast schedules, yet being unable to satisfy the demand. The answer was not to build more articulated streamliners, which would have meant the eventual scrapping of all the passenger equipment in existence, but to build a separate Diesel locomotive that could be hooked onto the front end of standard equipment. This would call for more power, since standard trains were heavy, but power was no longer an insurmountable barrier. In other words, it was time to move out onto the main line in full competition with steam.

All the developments that had gone on before—the early rail cars, the gas engines, the distillates, the 201 Diesels, the articulated streamliners—pointed to 1934 as the year of decision.

Chapter 4

THE MAIN-LINE PASSENGER
LOCOMOTIVE

Though the year of decision was at hand, the climate in 1934 was hardly favorable to the conduct of brave experiments. Nobody really knew if a separate Diesel locomotive could be made. And even if the railroads had been confident of its merits, many lines were in receivership and had little money to risk.

Then there was Electro-Motive, a mere skeleton of its former robust self. The depression had practically ended the production of rail cars, and only a small corps of the faithful remained. Yet the finger was pointing straight toward Dilworth at the Winton plant in Cleveland. There was nobody else in the country so qualified to take the next step as he.

Dilworth had his two draftsmen Everett Hanna and Bill Yirava. He also had his boardinghouse dream of 1910 that some day a Diesel would pull the Twentieth Century Limited. And he had faith.

While Dilworth began dreaming dreams over his drawing board, many railroads were still trying to meet the new high-speed schedules with steam, but when a steam locomotive heavy enough to pull a long train went beyond 70, it did one of two things. Either the wheels pounded the track, often leaping clear of the track for a fraction of an inch, or the nose of the monster began swaying back and forth. If you corrected for one weakness, you enhanced the other. Until the high drivers and connecting rods were eliminated, it would never be any different. There was a ceiling of size and speed beyond which the steam locomotive wouldn't go. So the railroads waited impatiently on Cleveland, where an engineer and a couple of draftsmen were working.

"I decided to pick the three best steam locomotives in passenger service and better their performance," Dilworth says. "I took for my models the J3 of the New York Central, the S4 of the Burlington, and the F2 of the Milwaukee."

These were all big Hudsons, a name that refers to the 4-6-4 wheel arrangement, four idle wheels under the pilot, six high driving wheels next, and four more idle wheels under the cab.

The next thing was to get the money to build a couple of experimental locomotives that would outperform these Hudsons. Both Hamilton and Dilworth began working on General Motors. Dilworth spent quite a bit of time in Detroit, talking to anyone who would listen. He talked to Kettering, to John W. Pratt and O. E. Hunt. Hamilton went from Kettering to Alfred P. Sloan. The upshot was that General Motors came through with an appropriation of a half million dollars.

The next question was how to build the locomotive. To this problem, Dilworth brought his uncommon ability to reduce complicated matters to simple terms. To him, any locomotive could be reduced to a formula that required only arithmetic for its solution.

From the railroad, you learned the weight of the train you would have to pull and the steepest grade you would have to pull it up. To these data you then applied certain simple formulas for train resistance and grade resistance, and you came out with the required weight of the locomotive. Not until you talked about the speed at which the locomotive was to pull the train did you concern yourself with horsepower. To arrive at this, you translated the weight of the locomotive into tractive effort, a figure expressed in pounds. You multiplied this by the desired speed in miles per hour, divided by 308, and you had the horsepower required in the Diesel engine.

"All railroading," Dilworth says, "is based on one thing—that 1 horsepower equals 33,000 foot-pounds per minute. And you juggle that and toss it around and set it to music and play it on a flute. And you make it come out a locomotive."

Playing these simple tunes on his flute—i.e., his slide rule—Dilworth determined that some 3,600 horsepower would be needed to better the performance of the Hudsons. This much power could be obtained from four 201A twelve-cylinder Diesel engines, each delivering 900 horsepower.

When it came to housing these engines and their accompanying electrical equipment, Dilworth decided to use steel boxcars. To understand why Dilworth selected the boxcar, instead of designing a more original and impressive home for the smooth power of the Diesel, we must learn how he feels about boxcars.

To most of us a boxcar is an unlovely and practical hunk of rolling stock, a rectangular beast of burden without grace or appeal, hardly worth a second glance.

To Dilworth a boxcar is a thing of beauty and a marvel of design. He brings to it an admiration usually reserved for a fine sculpture or a painting. He likes it because it is simple and flexible and able to stand up longer under conditions of extreme neglect than anything that rolls along on wheels.

"They've been trying to make boxcars cheaper for a long time," he says, "and the only way they could make them cheaper was to make them simpler; so the boxcar has become a very simple machine indeed."

So when Dilworth built his first Diesel-electric passenger locomotives, he selected the sturdy, economical boxcar. Since one boxcar could hardly house four Diesel engines plus all the necessary electrical equipment, Dilworth decided to use two boxcars, thus dividing the 3,600-horsepower locomotive into two equal parts, coupled together. If necessary, they could be used as separate locomotives of 1,800 horsepower each, and to this end he equipped each car with a set of controls.

Dilworth insists that the creation of those first locomotives was not a problem of invention but merely one of proportion. He points out that there was nothing in them that hadn't existed before. The 201A engines had been built and proved as power plants for the small articulated streamliners. The electrical equipment already existed. Dilworth installed a four-cylinder air compressor that had never been used before, but the four cylinders were merely duplicates of cylinders that had already been built for another air compressor; so even that wasn't new. Boxcars weren't new.

Yet, when all these preexisting items had been put together, the result was something new under the sun. For time was to prove this to be the first commercially successful high-speed Diesel passenger locomotive ever built—a locomotive that could be coupled onto any standard train.

Nobody had ever put that much horsepower over four axles before. The Union Pacific streamliners had used six to eight axles. Dilworth is proud of the fact that he "got a locomotive into a simple four-axle car" instead of some fancy special design. And it must be remembered that this parent of all Diesel passenger locomotives was conceived and brought forth not by a big staff of experts, but by one engineer and two draftsmen. It was done at a time when Electro-Motive was nothing more than a stripped-down outfit attached to the Winton Engine Company in Cleveland.

So it happened that the 511 and 512 made their bow to the railroads disguised as boxcars, two powerful performers in drab dress. Considering their brilliant future, this was somewhat like an Olympic dash champion walking out on the cinder track in overalls and blue workshirt.

The introduction of this locomotive to the railroads occasioned some lively clashes arising from the bluntness of Dilworth and the stubbornness of the railroads. The task of presenting the locomotive—still unbuilt—fell to Dilworth and O. F. Brookmeyer, the sales manager.

"Brookmeyer and I decided that in offering the 511 and

512 we'd go to the toughest so-and-so in the railroad business," Dilworth recalls. "We picked Emerson of the B. and O. We figured if we could convince him a lot of others would go along."

They approached George H. Emerson, chief of motive power and equipment, telling him that they wanted to put the new Diesel on his railroad for tests at no cost to the B. and O. Emerson, who was willing to spend a considerable sum to help develop a Diesel locomotive, asked why General Motors was willing to pick up the check.

"So you fellows won't tell us how to build it," Dilworth said flatly.

Dilworth knew that over the years the railroads had developed many pet ideas on what constituted a locomotive, and each railroad had a different set of ideas. The railroads had been the real designers of steam locomotives, rather than the locomotive shops. The result had been custom-made locomotives of infinite variety. Dilworth wanted none of that with the new Diesel. He wanted a simple, unadorned standard product, suitable for all railroads.

This idealistic concept would have been a designer's heaven, but it ran into trouble from the beginning. Emerson was willing to try the two-unit experimental locomotive and even wanted to buy one 1,800-horsepower unit in addition, but he wanted the third unit modified for a special type of coupler.

The same difficulty occurred when Electro-Motive approached John Purcell, mechanical chief of the Santa Fe.

"What kind of an underframe does it have?" Purcell wanted to know.

"Oh," Dilworth replied indifferently, "we welded together

some needles and hairpins and stuff—made it strong enough to support the machinery."

Railroads had a horror of welding. Steam locomotives had cast-steel underframes, big, solid, and all in one piece. A welded underframe would come apart at the joints.

Dilworth's reaction was to tell both railroads that if they wanted such modifications to go look elsewhere (knowing full well they had nowhere else to look), but the orders were taken nevertheless. The Santa Fe ordered two units with cast-steel underframes, and the B. and O. ordered one modified for its special coupler. Thus not two, but five, 1,800-horsepower units were being built at the same time, three of them in the General Electric shops at Erie and two at the St. Louis Car Company.

It cannot be said categorically that the 511 and 512 were a rousing success from the start. When Dilworth recalls the bugs, the breakdowns, and the on-the-spot repairs needed to keep them going, he is inclined to chew on his pipestem and become lost in sorrowful memories. At some time or other, nearly everything went wrong—the engine, the electrical equipment, the structure itself.

He finally explains it this way:

"The 511 and 512 proved that a Diesel locomotive couldn't be built and it wouldn't run—but when it did run, it would pull a train."

This doesn't quite express it, so he tries again:

"When you're contemplating anything new, you ask yourself three questions: Can I make it? Will it work? Is it worthwhile? Well, we could barely make it, it wouldn't work worth a darn, but it was so worthwhile that it had to go on. How does that Biblical phrase go? 'No man, having put his hand to the plough, and looking back, is fit for the kingdom of God.' That's the fix we were in."

The anomaly of a near failure that was a conspicuous success can best be explained by the experience of the B. and O., when it used the experimental Diesel on its maiden run to Chicago. Emerson had doubted that a 3,600-horsepower engine was powerful enough to pull a train over Sand Patch Hill, the most critical grade on the line. The steam locomotives used over that difficult grade were rated at more than 5,000 horsepower, and he predicted that 5,000 would be required in a Diesel.

But when the Diesel made its first run from Baltimore to Chicago and pulled into the Chicago station on time, Emerson was enthusiastic. He told the welcoming committee that the new Diesel was the "pullingest animal on rails!"

Dilworth couldn't resist his dig. "Do you still think it takes 5,000 horsepower, Colonel?"

"I don't know," Emerson replies, "but whatever it takes, that baby's got it!"

This acclaim from the toughest so-and-so in the business was the official seal of approval. B. and O.'s new unit was put to work pulling the *Royal Blue*, and Santa Fe's two units hauled the *Super Chief* between Los Angeles and Chicago in the unheard-of time of 39¾ hours.

The new plant

These new passenger locomotives went into service in the summer and fall of 1935. While they were ironing out their troubles and winning their spurs, a fine new plant was rising on the outskirts of La Grange, Illinois.

The fall before, the few key men remaining in Electro-Motive had discussed the need for such a plant. Obviously, it was far from satisfactory to contract the building of these locomotives in car shops all over the country. Apparently the railroads were going to want quite a few of these strange, smokeless, steamless locomotives, in which case it was time for Electro-Motive to build its own shop and thus control the production.

Dilworth visualized perhaps a million-dollar layout in Cleveland, in connection with the Winton Engine Company. He decided that to shake this much money out of General Motors in a depression year would require the shock treatment.

"General Motors executives that fall were having a family party at White Sulphur Springs," he recalls. "I managed to get myself put on the program for a short talk. They had a lot of speakers that afternoon, and most of them overran their time. When they got around to me, there wasn't much time left; so I didn't waste any words.

"I was talking to automobile men. So I told them their cars and trucks were nothing but rubber-tired toys. I told 'em that if they filled the highways solid with these toys they wouldn't be able to do a quarter of the transportation business of the country. (In 1950, in spite of the sensational postwar rise of the trucking industry, the railroads were hauling nearly five times the ton-miles of all trucks.) I reminded 'em that the railroads were still the workhorses of the country."

The audience applauded. There is something in human nature that responds to frankness and toughness of statement. The automobile men were told off, and they loved it.

"Hamilton was at the meeting," Dilworth remembers. "Where I had my sights set on a million-dollar shop, Hamilton had in mind something much bigger. While I was putting in my two cents' worth, Hamilton got an appropriation for no less than six million."

In March, 1935, while the new passenger units were getting their finishing touches at St. Louis and Erie, the first spadeful of earth was turned at La Grange for Hamilton's plant, the first Diesel-locomotive shop in the world.

Redesign

The locomotives hadn't been in service long before it became necessary to redesign them for production at La Grange. The steam engineers who ran those first locomotives didn't like the idea of sitting in the very front end of a locomotive going a hundred miles an hour. They missed the protection of the long boiler and dreaded the results of hitting a truck, or even a cow. Another trouble was "sleeper flicker," a kind of hypnosis induced by watching the railroad ties flick by underneath the front end. (Sleeper is the British word for a railroad tie.)

It was decided to move the engineer's cab up and back, behind a rounded nose. Though this may sound simple, it caused radical changes in the over-all design, among them the elimination of the boxcar. First, with the cab taking up the space over the front truck, the heavy generator and engine could no longer be kept squarely over the bolster and axle, but had to be moved to the center of the car, between front and rear trucks. In order to support this weight, boxcar construction had to be abandoned in favor of the truss. People who look at the sleek modern locomotive with its row of portholes on each side often assume that this bit of romantic styling was borrowed from the ocean liner. Instead, the portholes were the result of the truss construction of the sidewalls. The diagonal members of the truss no longer permitted the large rectangular windows of the 511-512; so portholes were placed between diagonals.

During the next few years, Dilworth presided over a rapidly expanding engineering department in the new plant at La Grange. Under S. H. Cowin, La Grange designed its own motors and generators, and under Eugene Kettering a new series of engines was designed to replace the 201s, and these were also put into production at La Grange. Known as the 567 series, they came in three sizes, a six-cylinder 600-horsepower engine, a twelve-cylinder 1,000-horsepower, and a sixteen-cylinder 1,350-horsepower. Later an eight-cylinder model was added. Two of the 1,000-horsepower engines went into a locomotive unit, giving it 2,000 horses. Two and three of these units, combined into a 4,000- or 6,000-horsepower locomotive, began pulling the crack trains of the country on unheard-of schedules. These strange, powerful beasts, with their raucous horns, and their humming and smokeless speed, were given a name. They were called "Streamliners."

It was no easy job for Dilworth and his growing staff of engineers to keep the Streamliners running smoothly. From the first, they ran into the grim fact that this new type of motive power made demands on materials and parts never before encountered in railroading. In building the Diesel, Dil-worth and his men had tried to use as many parts familiar to railroad men as possible. This made sense from the standpoint of service. But though many of these parts had been adequate for steam operation, they proved sadly lacking for the Diesel.

Wheels are an example. Dilworth explained why steel that might be all right for a steam-locomotive wheel was no good on a Diesel:

"A Diesel locomotive," he says, "first of all is two or more electric locomotives down on the rail. Over them is a platform carrying a powerhouse big enough for a small city and complete with everything but a brick stack. To get this big powerhouse inside railroad tunnels and other tight spots, the platform must be kept low, and that means small wheels (steam driving wheels are much larger). About forty inches in diameter is the limit.

"These wheels not only carry the weight of the locomotive but transmit the power of the engine by pulling on the rail. The small area of contact between the wheel and the rail is doing a lot of work, and work is a destructive thing. The small wheel of the Diesel does more work than the large wheel of a steam locomotive, partly because it is smaller and partly because the Diesel can start faster. Now, you can make a wheel that will resist this work by using very hard and brittle steel, but that kind of steel will crack when heated by the brake shoes on long steep mountain grades. So a compromise had to be found between the 'shelling' caused by work and the 'cracking' caused by heat. This resulted in many years of mutual development with a number of steel mills in an effort to find a better chemistry for the steel, better forging and rolling methods, and better heat-treatment for the finished wheel."

This long and unspectacular campaign to improve wheels was matched by a campaign to improve nearly everything else that went into the locomotive. Fifteen years of constant effort went into improving the metallurgy and design of the Diesel-engine pistons, with the result that the average life of a piston was raised from 80,000 miles to nearly a million.

Dilworth needed a large staff of specialists for no other reason than to upgrade materials and parts, metal, wire, and structure, to equal the high demands of the new Streamliners that were beginning to take over the main-line passenger service of our railroads.

With the Streamliners, the age of color arrived on the nation's railroads. Replacing the drab, dark steam locomotives, the sleek Diesels were as brilliant with gold, red, yellow, and blue as a fall landscape.

Dilworth called them circus wagons and considers them just a step on the way to the main job of the railroad, which is to pull freight. At this point, he likes to summarize the development up to 1939.

"The articulated trains solved the problems of speed on the main line," he says, "but because they were fixed-consist they were limited in their use. The railroads demanded a separate locomotive, and we obliged with the 511 and 512, later modified into our Streamliners.

"These Streamliners were bought neither for their economy nor for their reliability. Nobody knew at the time whether they would save money, or stand up. They were bought for one purpose only, and that was speed.

"But as we learned how to build them and the railroads began accumulating records on them, we all learned that they were both economical and reliable. They were cheaper to operate, and when their hours of availability in a year were considered, they were even cheaper in first cost.

"When the railroads discovered this, the next step was apparent. It was time for the Diesel to cease being a circus wagon and start pulling freight."

Why couldn't steam do this job?

In Dilworth's mind, steam had outlived its usefulness by almost fifteen years. Since he had first had anything to do with railroads—around 1910—he had watched boxcars getting bigger, trains getting longer, and passenger service getting faster. This trend accelerated during World War I and continued through the twenties as an economy measure.

To haul these longer, heavier, and faster trains, steam locomotives had been getting bigger, more unwieldly, and less efficient. Dilworth describes the losing battle thus:

"The only way to make a steam locomotive more powerful is to increase the number of square feet of heating surface in the boiler. Since tunnels and railway platforms and the width between rails all limit the height and width of an engine, the only way to increase the heating surface is to make the boiler longer. But if it gets too long, the fire gets cold before it reaches the far end of the boiler. Thus there is a practical limit to how large a steam locomotive can be."

Still the effort went on, until finally there was produced what Dilworth calls a monstrosity. He has a picture of it, a photostated drawing of a Mallet Articulated Triplex, a behemoth weighing 425 tons, with twenty-four driving wheels.

To Dilworth's way of thinking, giants like the Mallet were not only inefficient, they were destructive of the track.

It was about 1924, Dilworth recalls, that locomotive shops gave up the struggle to produce locomotives equal to the demands of the railroads. When they threw up their hands, the railroads tried to carry on in their own shops. This began in 1926 and went on for a few years without success. Finally, in 1929, Dilworth says: "The guys who had the shovel and the keys to the strongbox quit scooping out the dough."

Thus Dilworth would mark the headstone of the steam locomotive in this fashion:

> Sick in 1924
> Died in 1926
> Death recognized in 1929

By the time Dilworth was ready to tackle the job of building freight locomotives, the Diesel was more than ten years overdue.

Experimental rail car at General Electric plant in which early ideas for electric transmission were tried out

First Electro-Motive rail car, delivered in 1924

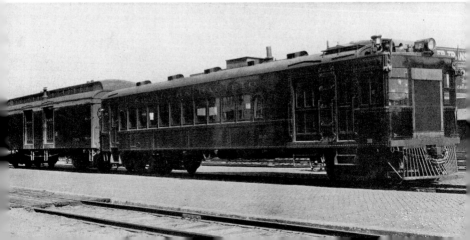

First building of Electro-Motive: parts warehouse in Cleveland in 1926

Electro-Motive rail cars rose to this 800-horsepower gas-electric freight locomotive in 1928

The parents of modern American trains (1934)—Union Pacific City of Salina (left) and the Burlington Pioneer Zephyr (right)

The United States' first separate main-line Diesel locomotive to go into revenue service (1935): General Motors 1,800-horsepower locomotive for the B. and O. Royal Blue

Original Santa Fe Super Chief (1935), drawn by 3,600-horsepower General Motors locomotive

Diesel becomes lord of the rails, 1939: North America's first main-line Diesel freight locomotive, 5,400 horsepower

Diesel locomotive pools begin to appear on American railroads, 1939

Original manufacturing plant of Electro-Motive at La Grange, Illinois, 1935, 205,000 square feet

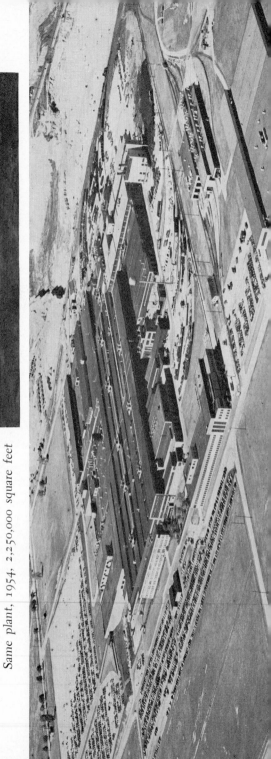

Same plant, 1954, 2,250,000 square feet

Chapter 5

THE FREIGHT LOCOMOTIVE

For Dilworth this job meant the consumption of great quantities of grocery-store wrapping paper and the manipulation of an assortment of slide rules that included a fabulous spiral 105-inch job that carried logarithms to seven decimal places. Both wrapping paper and slide rules are legends at La Grange.

"My father told me once upon a time," says Dilworth, "that a slide rule is a mechanical brain to help out a man with a wooden head. I usually have one in my pocket, another on the desk, and my spiral one in the drawer of the desk.

"I remember toward the end of World War I we had to cut a helical gear that had been made in England, and when we tried to set up an American machine to match something made in England we ran into trouble. To find those gear combinations, I'd shoot the problem off on my 10-inch slide rule and find three or four combinations that looked nearly right. Then I'd take those and run them through the 105-inch rule and reduce the combinations to one or two. On problems like that, you can let slide rules do most of the work, and if you have to be more accurate, you can take a Monroe calculating machine and go down to ten decimal places.

"A slide rule is a good start for anything. In most railroading it's all we ever need because there is some other factor in the problem that isn't even as accurate as the slide rule."

The wrapping paper was attached underneath his desk, at one side, so that he could pull it out from its roll and lay it across the desk. It was 36 inches wide, ample enough to give scope to the soft black pencil with which he translated his ideas into pictures.

When he began anything like the freight locomotive, Dilworth would pull out a great expanse of wrapping paper, start drawing, then sit and wait for his mind to work. After a while he'd sketch some more, then wait for his mind again.

"After that," he says, "I'd probably tear it off, stuff it in the wastebasket, and start over again."

Few of these wrapping-paper sketches have been saved, chiefly because they have been rough ideas, to be carried out in detail by someone else. Now and then a piece of paper would be returned to his desk, much to his embarrassment, particularly in the case of an electrical hookup that didn't work. He depended on expert electrical layout men to translate his hookups into workable schemes.

When Dilworth discusses his roll of wrapping paper, it is plain to see that an expanse of blank paper has a fascination for him. It is an invitation to create, a spur that brings into play all his accumulated knowledge of what constitutes a locomotive. He doesn't take kindly to the drudgery of design—the hookups, the small modifications necessary to please a customer or simplify manufacture—but when he is asked to proportion a new locomotive, the inner light begins to burn, the outside world fades, the wrapping paper comes out, and the big black pencil goes into action.

The job Dilworth tackled now was a special challenge. The railroads had been saying that there were some kinds of work that the Diesel wouldn't be big enough to handle. They admitted that it was fast, but they doubted that it was powerful.

Electro-Motive's response to this was to set about building the most powerful locomotive ever put on the rails. For his steam prototype, Dilworth picked the Santa Fe–type 2-10-2, a monster with ten driving wheels.

In order to outdo this giant, he produced a four-part locomotive, each part or car having a sixteen-cylinder 1,350-horsepower engine, a generator, and four driving axles. He permanently coupled two of these units to form a 2,700-horsepower locomotive, providing only one set of controls for the two. Then, by adding a second combination, he had a 5,400-horsepower locomotive, weighing some 440 tons.

The story of how this experimental locomotive went into service late in 1939 and through 1940, traveling 83,000 miles over all types of terrain, outpulling any locomotive ever built, has been told elsewhere. Dilworth sums it up in a single sentence, when he says:

"It pulled a lot of trains in two and others uphill."

Yet Dilworth, surprisingly, considers this first freight locomotive the biggest boner of his career.

The trouble was in the inflexible coupling of two units into 2,700 horsepower. This meant that the railroad's choice lay

between a 2,700-horsepower locomotive and a 5,400-horse-
power engine, with nothing in between. It was either half a
locomotive or a whole one. The half locomotive was too light
for some work, and the whole locomotive was too heavy for
much of the work.

Dilworth wanted to correct his boner by separating the locomotive into independent units of 1,350 horsepower each, so
that they could be used singly, or in combinations of two,
three, and four. Such a locomotive would be able to do 85
per cent of the hauling work of the country. And this, in turn,
would permit the quantity production of locomotives.

Before anything could be done, however, the United States
was at war with the Axis powers and all designs were frozen.
Electro-Motive was stuck with its superpowerful prodigy and
could do nothing about it.

As it turned out, Dilworth's boner worked out all right for
Uncle Sam. The two-hemisphere war, calling for heavy shipments of goods both to Atlantic and Pacific ports, put a
heavy strain on the railroads, many of which soon reached the
saturation point.

On the Santa Fe, for example, which runs through desert
country, water became the critical factor. The more the traffic
increased, the more water had to be hauled to desert division
points. Hundreds of tank cars carrying millions of gallons of
water had to be used merely to keep other trains running.

The Diesel needed no water stops. Furthermore, it could
run from Chicago to Los Angeles without relief, whereas six
or eight steam locomotives might be used on the same run.
On the Santa Fe and elsewhere, the big freight Diesels went
into service, breaking bottlenecks that threatened to choke

the pace of the war on the home front. Electro-Motive built some four hundred of its freight locomotives, known as the FT, and the supplies they hauled helped to break the backs of the Central powers. Dilworth's boner happened just in time to help save the nation.

The dynamic brake

"These freight locomotives introduced the dynamic brake into general use," Dilworth recalls.

The dynamic brake wasn't new. It was a system of using the traction motors as generators, to retard the driving axle instead of propelling it. It had been used on streetcars, as well as on the electrified Milwaukee lines to "pump power back into the trolley line to help another train up the other side of the hill."

Where there is no trolley, the power generated by retarding the train has to be dissipated as heat. An experimental turbine locomotive that used the dynamic brake in this fashion—without a trolley—was being tested about the time Electric-Motive's big FTs were going into service, and Electro-Motive watched its performance with interest.

"The reaction was that the turbine locomotive wasn't so hot," Dilworth says, "but it sure had a nice brake. The enthusiasm for the brake was enough to tip the scales in favor of putting it on the Diesel."

Electro-Motive's version of the dynamic brake was designed to control downhill a train of the same weight as the locomotive could pull up that hill. The engineer applied it by operating a lever, meanwhile watching a meter to see that he didn't overdo the use of motors as generators. It was used on hills, rather than in bringing a train to a stop on level ground. The brake was a success. During the war years, when metal was precious stuff, it saved thousands of car wheels and brake shoes.

"For instance," Dilworth says, "there is a long, nasty downgrade west of Cajon Pass that is used both by the Union Pacific and Santa Fe. This grade is about twenty-five miles long, and there are some large shops at the bottom. In steam days it wasn't uncommon for the San Bernardino shops to change 2,500 pairs of wheels in a day because of the overheating that resulted from bringing freight trains down the grade. Today, I doubt if they handle 2,500 wheels in a month.

"I always liked one of the first stories that came out about the dynamic brake. I was traveling with it to watch it, and as we were coming down a mean grade on the Santa Fe, the old road foreman operating the locomotive became quite enthusiastic about the behavior of the brake. Said we ought to have them on all locomotives.

"I told him to take it easy. There was a question of dollars and cents that would determine whether the brake ever became popular. It would have to earn a good return on a large amount of money before the Santa Fe or any other railroad would buy it in quantity. He wanted to know how much it would have to earn.

"Well," I said, "it's got to save between $2,000 and $3,000 a year in brake shoes and wheels to pay a decent return on the investment. To be a real good investment it ought to pay $4,000.

"The old man thought that over for quite a while, and

then he said: 'Well, I don't know whether this thing will save the Santa Fe railroad $2,000 a year or not, but I do know that it will save me a pair of woolen socks every time I come down this hill.'

"I waited for more, and it was forthcoming. He said: 'When I bring a train down this here mountain on air, I claw up a pair of woolen stockings all to pieces with my toenails. With this contraption all I got to do is sit here and pick my nose.'"

Dilworthian salesmanship

It's an odd fact that, in spite of the wonderful wartime performance of the big FTs with their dynamic brakes, some railroad officials were still unconvinced of their merits. With a background of 100 years of steam, they still couldn't believe that Diesels could equal the performance of some of their pet creations. Thus shortly after the war ended, the president of one Western road made some disparaging remarks about the upstart Diesel to an Electro-Motive salesman.

"When you can equal the big boy up there," he said, pointing to the picture of a steam locomotive on the wall of his office, "come around and we'll talk business."

When Dilworth heard this later, he decided that the challenge called for blunt action. The fact that the "big boy" was a locomotive in the 7,000-horsepower range, a monster with sixteen driving wheels, meant nothing to him. Steam locomotives seldom delivered their rated horsepower. They were affected by soot, scale, and cold weather, factors that meant nothing to a Diesel. Dilworth knew that his 5,400-horsepower freight job could hold its own against the big boy. He wasted no time in getting to the telephone.

"I hear you've been taking advantage of the ignorance of one of our men," he said to the official. "I'd like to make a prediction. If you'll put our four-unit freight locomotive alongside your big boy on that hill out in Utah, we'll push your big boy *so far back into Lionel's window with the rest of the toys* that no one will ever talk about it again."

An associate once tried to describe the force of Dilworth's personality by saying: "He can cold-reason an engineer into a corner, humorously disarm a self-assured railroad man, and enthuse a wooden Indian."

The incident just related is an example of humorous disarmament. The official's answer is not recorded, but it may be assumed that he enjoyed the sally. Railroad officers seldom took offense at Dilworth's toughness of speech. As a species, they were reasonably tough themselves. They understood the language. Their relationship with Dick was informally profane. Dilworth had earned the respect of these men by not overselling his own product. They had learned from experience that his predictions of performance were usually accurate.

The era covered by this chapter was a climactic one. In the brief period between 1934 and the outbreak of war in 1941, Dilworth's creativeness came to full flower. In this highly active span of 7 years, his accumulated knowledge of railroading, internal-combustion engines, and electricity came powerfully to bear on the job that had to be done—the revolutionary task of producing a new kind of motive power for America's main-line railroads. To sum up:

He began the period by laying out the power cars for the

small streamliners that were to startle the traveling public during the years of the depression.

These trains educated the public to high-speed passenger schedules and to luxurious appointments, but their motive power was no answer to the need of the railroads. The power car of a streamliner was articulated to the next car in the train—meaning that one truck supported the rear of the power car and the front of the following car. Thus, the power car— i.e., locomotive—could be used only on that train and no other.

Diesel-electric power could be made general only by producing an independent locomotive with standard coupler that could be hooked onto the front of any passenger train. It would have to be powerful enough to pull the heavy "black" trains of the day.

Though the transition may sound simple in the telling, nobody knew if it could be done. Yet Dilworth, with only a couple of draftsmen for staff, designed the first commercially successful passenger locomotives. After the usual period of modification, these locomotives proved so economical and swift that they sealed the doom of steam in passenger service.

Then, to prove that the Diesel-electric was a workhorse as well as a racehorse, Dilworth and his growing staff of engineers produced the powerful freight locomotives that were to prove lifesavers in World War II, and after the war were to go on to replace steam on all the nation's main lines.

Dilworth was now, in 1941, fifty-six years old. He had achieved his dream of 1910 to produce the motive power that would one day pull the Twentieth Century Limited, but to him the job was far from finished. There were the secondary and branch lines to conquer. The job ahead was to develop these pioneer prewar Diesel-electrics to the point where a few simple designs would be able to handle all the needs of the railroads, not simply those of the main lines.

This task, however, would have to wait for some five years, until the factories of the nation could resume their peacetime objectives. Right now, there was a war on, and plants like the Electro-Motive Division of La Grange, with their engineering know-how, would have to do some strange and wonderful things in line of duty.

Chapter 6

ENGINES FOR WAR

For Dilworth the war years, aside from such work as had to be done on the passenger and freight locomotives, involved some fast improvising to provide horsepower for the supply lines and the battle fronts. He worked overtime to convert the regular locomotive engines—the 567s—to various war uses, and is proud of what his department accomplished here.

His fastest bit of work, however, occurred on another engine that came to be known as the Quad. In 1942, with German submarines sinking Allied ships at an appalling rate, the Navy was in a hurry to get engines for its 110-foot subchasers. For this craft, General Motors Research had designed a light powerful Diesel called the 184, an engine developing 1,200 horsepower. The 184 was being readied for production at La Grange.

Unfortunately, the Navy couldn't wait for the bugs to be ironed out of this highly precise and lightweight power plant.

Hulls, they said, were waiting, and they needed engines right now. In this emergency, R. K. Evans came to La Grange and suggested to Dilworth that they try to use General Motors' truck and bus Diesel, an engine known as the 6-71, developing about 225 horsepower. As Dilworth recalls it:

"Bob Evans said that two of these engines had been geared together on one shaft with pretty good results, and he wanted to know could I put four of them into one propeller shaft. That would make an engine of 900 horsepower, and two of them totaling 1,800 horsepower would be about enough for the subchaser. These would do for the emergency, and when the 184s were ready, the Quads (so-called because they were four engines in one) would be taken out and the 184s put in. I said, yes, we could make it, but it wouldn't be any good, and he said, 'Make it.'

"So I threw together a gearbox that would take four 6-71 engines pumping into one big bull gear which turned the propeller shaft. The gearbox was welded out of such plate as we could find, the gear was roughly cut . . . the whole thing was a pretty crude job. Got it together in about five weeks; so you know just how crude it was.

"The only virtue of the whole thing was that each engine fed into the gearbox through a clutch—an automobile disk clutch. The main idea was that if an engine failed it could be uncoupled from the rest, but actually the clutch had a more important function than that. Trying to get four six-cylinder engines to work on one shaft was a problem. If the engines didn't work at precisely the same speed, or if the four crankshafts were at slightly the wrong angle, violent torsional vibrations could be set up. We put the clutches in to take care of that. As soon as the vibrations started, the clutches would slip a little, change the angle of the crankshaft, and the vibrations would stop. They acted as flexible couplings that allowed the engines to adjust themselves so they didn't quarrel."

The Navy looked at the engine and said it wouldn't work. It would shake itself to pieces. They set out to prove this was true, and Dilworth had much private enjoyment as he watched them in their attempts to catch the Quad misbehaving.

"They sent up Commander Den Hartog, an expert on engines, and he came along with two carloads of instruments and a whole crew of technicians. Den Hartog would keep the engines shut down for a while, then clutch them at the exact angle that he thought would give the worst vibrations. Then he'd start the four engines all at once.

"There was an immediate vibration that he could see on his oscillograph. But unfortunately, in order to get it recorded on a tape, he had to flap down the cover of the opening he was looking through and push a button, and while he was doing that the vibrations would disappear. He tried for a month without catching the vibrations."

By this time, the 184 engine was in production, and the mischievous Quad engine that should have been bad but wasn't was shoved under a bench and forgotten. But not for long.

"Some of our men went down to Washington and found a use for it. By this time the Navy had come along with another boat, the LCI (Landing Craft, Infantry). It was a clinker-built boat forward, a Japanese sampan amidship, and a Kanawha River mud boat aft. Well, it had to have an engine;

so the Quad was pulled out from under the bench and made
the official engine for the LCI. I think some 3,500 of those
Quad combinations were made and installed and used during
the war."

Dilworth never thought much of his gearbox and the
clutches that enabled four engines to work in harmony. It was
just one of those things that had to be done in war. So he
was much surprised when a "brass-bound admiral" showed up
at the end of the war, and with much ceremony handed him
a certificate of commendation for his engineering achievements for the Navy. He thought it was for his work on the
567 engines used to power the large LSTs (Landing Ship,
Tanks), something in which he took great pride.

"When I looked at the certificate and found it was on ac-
count of the Quads, I brought it home without ever showing
it to anybody at the plant." At this point, Dilworth reluctantly
waves at the library wall. "That's the certificate there. The side
that tells what it's for is turned to the wall. When you have
to let a clutch slip to get rid of vibrations, you have a mechanical monstrosity."

It may have been all of that, but it worked. It enabled mass-
produced truck and bus engines to be used in seagoing craft
and thus provided power for war when it was needed.

Postwar redesign

From 1945 on, with war restrictions lifted, the age of
the Diesel locomotive came on with dizzy speed. But though
the demand of the railroads for this new motive power ex-
ceeded the ability of Electro-Motive to supply it, there were

times when the evolution of the Diesel threatend to go off course. More than once, Dilworth found it necessary to grab hold of the sweep and steer the craft.

Despite the fact that the wartime FTs could be used only as a 2,700-horsepower or a 5,400-horsepower locomotive, with nothing in between, railroads began demanding a larger locomotive.

By 1945, the Diesel era was 10 years old, and by this time Dilworth was convinced that the true path of development was not in big single units, but in smaller units that could be hooked together. The proper thing to do was to divide the locomotive into four units of 1,350 horsepower each. These could be used singly, in twos, threes, or fours, depending on the job to be done. Units of 1,350 could be manufactured in quantity, with a great saving in cost, and bigness could be achieved simply by adding units. From the standpoint of both manufacture and operation this was the common-sense course.

But some railroads were still thinking in terms of steam, and a steam locomotive wasn't large unless the power was in a single package. They wanted a big Diesel, and it had to be one Diesel, not several.

There were long debates at La Grange over the matter. Railroad men came there with orders in their pockets, if Electro-Motive would build a super-Diesel. But Dilworth refused to be budged, and there were those who privately cussed him for being bullheaded, obstreperous, and unprogressive.

When a competitor announced its intention of complying with the request by building a Diesel to end all Diesels, the pressure on the engineering department increased, but Dilworth simply hung onto the oar and kept steering, let the oaths fall where they may. The competitor set about to build a 6,000-horsepower locomotive, all in one piece, while Electro-Motive continued to put out its four units of 1,350.

Dilworth knew what was behind this. He was aware that a certain railroad was hoping to duplicate in a Diesel one of its powerful electric locomotives, a monster that required a 156-pound track to support it. He knew that this didn't make sense. He wanted to sell locomotives not only to this line but to others that couldn't afford to rebuild their tracks to support mammoths.

Events proved him correct. In the end, the competitor could get no more than 3,000 horsepower into a single car, and even this unit had to be dropped before long. The campaign for bigness failed, and the flexible four-unit concept prevailed.

That question settled, Electro-Motive settled down to the job of building and selling locomotives. To Dilworth, who had seen his 40-year-old dream come true, and who had lived through the glorious adventure of experiment, doubt, and triumph, the job became less interesting. More and more of the time of his department was spent on routine work to expedite manufacturing. Another large part of the time was involved in minor changes to suit the desires of specific railroads. He recalls orders for locomotives from two Eastern railroads, one specifying 150 extras, the other 100 extras, and only two of the items overlapped. Because of demands like this, Dilworth figures that not more than 15 per cent of his time was occupied with what he considers "real engineering."

Chapter 7

ADVANCED ENGINEERING

To relieve Dilworth of this type of work, a new department was created for him called Advanced Engineering. With his customary frankness, Dilworth calls these his "declining years," and says he was "relegated" to the department and given the task of grinding out new devices later to be worked over by the regular engineering department before they went into production.

Actually his move to Advanced Engineering was like the opening of a floodgate, releasing a new torrent of creative energy. As he put it, "Being relieved of all the routine work of conducting an engineering department, I found it possible to do a little real engineering and believe that some advances in locomotive design came about at this time."

What he did specifically was to design a locomotive to meet the special needs of Australia, help create a military railway switcher, and design a locomotive for U.S. railroads that has since become Electro-Motive's best seller. This is a productive list of achievements for a man supposed to be in his "declining years."

The Australian locomotive was exciting to Dilworth because it posed special problems.

The Aussies wanted to Dieselize their Commonwealth Railroad, an 1,100-mile line between South Australia and West Australia along the shore of the Great Australian Bight. The line led through a country devoid of wood, water, and people, where the transportation of fuel and boiler water was the main business of the railroad. The advantage of the Diesel here was that it required no boiler water and not more than one or two fuel stops over the entire line.

The Australians wanted Electro-Motive's regular unit (now 1,500 horsepower), but because of the lighter tracks in their country they specified a weight of no more than 40,000 pounds per axle, some 20,000 pounds less than in the American version of the locomotive.

To solve this problem, Advanced Engineering went to a three-axle truck, or "bogie" as it is called in Australia. To build such a truck with all three axles motor-driven, yet to maintain the flexibility required for high-speed operation, was a goal that builders had unsuccessfully attempted to reach for many years.

Advanced Engineering solved it by adapting a design originally built for the Milwaukee, then abandoned. This truck, as modified by Dilworth's department, provided easy maintenance for the motor on the center axle, contained means for equalizing the power load on the three axles, and had an unusual spring suspension that gave a smooth ride. Provision was made to move wheels and brake shoes in or out, to allow the locomotive to be used on tracks of different gauges.

This new truck was so radically different from anything then in use, that Australia was afraid to try it. The joint product of Dilworth and his truck expert Martin Blomberg, the bogie did away with elliptic springs and employed four coil springs at the four corners. In place of a bolster it had an H frame.

To reassure Australia, Electro-Motive built two experimental trucks and put them under a flatcar loaded down with concrete blocks to equal the weight of a locomotive. This experimental car, fully instrumented, was tested on some of the roughest tracks in the Middle West and turned out to be one of the smoothest trucks ever built.

Australia was so pleased with its new locomotives that Fred Shea, chief engineer of the Clyde Engineering Company of Sydney, Australian manufacturer of Electro-Motive products, sent Dilworth a copy of the works of his favorite author, Rudyard Kipling. On the flyleaf was inscribed a poem "To R. M. Dilworth, with apologies to Rudyard Kipling:"

> On the road to Santa Fe
> Where the flying Diesels play,
> Rootin', tootin' on their whistles
> As they claim the right of way,
>
> Hear them screaming for the crossing,
> Dashing past the old steam pots.
> Stand aside, you puffing billies,
> We can't wait while you get hot!

Watch them ride into the depot,
Rolling down with conscious pride.
We're Dick Dilworth's pups, they holler,
He's the man who made us stride!

Many of the ideas developed for the Australian locomotives found their way into the MRS, a military railway switcher ordered by the U.S. Army. Developing the MRS also fell to Dilworth's Advanced Engineering Department.

The Army's specifications called for a locomotive that would operate in arctic or tropical weather and on every type of terrain. It required the light axle loading and the variable-gauge features of the Australian job. It was much more than a switcher. It was an all-purpose round-the-world locomotive. Dilworth's department met all these requirements in what Dilworth calls a "fairly good locomotive."

Detective story

The most astonishing thing about the Australian and military locomotives was the effect of the three-axle truck on tractive effort. Where the American 1,500-horsepower unit, with some 120 tons distributed over four axles, had a 43,000-pound tractive effort, the Australian job with the same weight distributed over six axles had a tractive effort of 60,000 pounds. This was nearly a 40 per cent improvement.

This semimiracle puzzled Dilworth, because there were no slippage formulas that would predict such a result. Dilworth doesn't like mysteries; so he undertook to discover a formula that would predict slippage accurately.

How he did this gives an insight into the workings of a

creative mind. It also has some of the fascinating turns of detective fiction.

Dilworth began his search with his customary healthy skepticism, which included a willingness to question the most hallowed tenets of the engineering textbook. He also brought to it a Dilworthian philosophy on how an engineer embarks on the ever-painful process of using his head. This is how he describes the birth pangs of a new engineering formula:

"It seems to be common practice to lay a piece of white paper on the table, take a pencil in your hand, and stare at the paper. But blank paper is a picture of total ignorance—it doesn't talk back to you very loudly. So, waiting for the paper to talk to you, you start doodling, and it's quite common to draw a horizontal line close to the bottom of the paper and then draw a vertical line close to the left-hand edge—and you still have nothing on the paper. Then, often as not, you will mark a zero down in the intersection of the two lines and call one line X and the other Y—and you still have nothing.

"Then you begin to wonder if there are any possible meanings to X and Y that might have a bearing on what you want to know. If you figure out something, you mark it down. You still have X and Y, but now they have a meaning, and it's the relationship of X to Y that is going to be of value to you. If X equals Y, you draw a straight line of 45 degrees, from the intersection to the upper right-hand corner of the paper, and you've finished.

"But ordinarily X doesn't equal Y, and so you begin to wonder where to put the line. Then you remember that you heard a story once, and you put down a dot to represent the story. Then you remember that somebody made an experiment on his own particular value of X and it came out a particular value for Y, and it wasn't exactly like the story, but you mark that down, too.

"And then, when from memory you put down every relationship between X and Y you can think of, you survey the paper and you finally decide, well, the line you are hunting for probably crosses O. Now you have one definite place and several very indefinite places. After staring at them for a while, you decide that you can take a broad piece of chalk, make a sweep with your arm, and draw a curve that sort of seems to follow the average values of X and Y.

"Having done that, you set down, probably on another piece of paper, all the different factors you think might have a bearing on the problem. Having done this, you start in to juggle them once more. You add exponents and coefficients and throw in constants, and finally you build a formula that will somewhere near reproduce the line you drew from the memories that you jotted down.

"You now have a start, and you say, well, this formula that I have constructed, which almost reproduces this line that I think is somewhere near where it ought to be, *is probably not so*, but it will do as a working tool until I learn better.

"So you start out, working as though that formula were correct. You build machines and test them, and you put down on the same piece of paper the results of those tests, and you find then that you can correct your formula so that it conforms more nearly to the test results. When you have done that *over and over*, you have a formula that is a working tool. *You still have no faith in it*, you know it is probably not nearly true, but it will do to work with until you learn better.

"Well, that formula may go on for years and years, and a business might be built up around it. It still wouldn't be right, but would get the results you need. The great trouble is that somebody comes and looks over your shoulder and sees what you are doing and asks, 'Where did you get that formula? That looks pretty good!' You tell him that you built it up slowly, and this is now what you believe is sufficiently accurate for all practical purposes; so your friend says, 'That ought to be published!' So he runs and puts it in a book and that book gets accepted as a textbook in the colleges, and the first thing you know your formula has become gospel.

"A great many of the formulas used in engineering have been made exactly that way. They're all right as long as you distrust them while you're using them, but if you believe them, you're likely to get into trouble."

This is an accurate description of how an empirical approximation becomes the "Law and the Prophets," thereafter to be devoutly studied by earnest students desiring to become engineers. And in the passage of time, teachers and students alike forget entirely that the law originally was only a good guess, based on observation.

Dilworth questions the law, wherever he encounters it, even though it has behind it the authority of centuries of acceptance. Thus, one reason why he was able to arrive at a successful formula to predict the slippage of the Military Railway Switcher was because he questioned a principle laid down by Leonardo da Vinci four and a half centuries before.

The famous Florentine had arrived at a "law," which, for lay understanding, might be stated something as follows: "If you place a load on a surface, then try to move it, the amount of surface in contact with the load doesn't affect the amount of friction developed. The only thing that affects friction is the total weight of the load." (*Ergo*, if you have two or three axles or larger or smaller driving wheels, the friction is the same.)

What da Vinci is reported to have done is stretch out a ship's cable on a dusty road and count the number of men it took to drag the cable down the road. Then he rolled up the cable and stoppered it so it wouldn't come unrolled and found it took the same number of men to drag it. So he devised the engineering "principle" that the unit loading of the surface is not a factor in the friction, only the total load.

When Dilworth went hunting for an already existing slippage formula, he found that there were no reliable ones in this country. In the United States, Dilworth explains, it has been the practice to make locomotives heavier if they slipped, thus burying our ignorance under the weight of steel on drivers. We could do this because we had good tracks in this country.

In Europe, on the other hand, where rails are lighter and there are fewer ties per mile, the practice is to use lighter locomotives. Thus Europeans are more troubled by slippage and have done much figuring on the subject.

So Dilworth collected some thirteen European formulas for slippage and tried to apply them to the Military Railway Switcher with its lighter axle loading. The result was thirteen different answers so widely at variance that he was afraid to use any of them.

Then came a bit of detective work worthy of *Dragnet*. Dilworth realized that these formulas had been built from experiments with specific locomotives in specific countries. But which countries and which locomotives? The formulas didn't say.

He studied the names attached to the formulas, and from the character of the name he tried to determine the country— whether French, German, Italian, Spanish, or Dutch. He then studied the dates on the formulas to learn the years in which the experiments had been conducted, after which he looked up the most common types of locomotives used in those years.

Now he was getting somewhere. He now knew the sizes of the driving wheels and the weights on drivers and could relate these facts to the thirteen formulas. As he studied the various types of locomotives and noted the different sizes of driving wheels, the thought occurred to him that perhaps the larger wheel made a difference. The larger the wheel, the more nearly the rail "wrapped around" the wheel, thus increasing the area of wheel in contact with the rail. Of course da Vinci had said that the area in contact didn't make any difference, that the friction would be the same whether the load rested on a pinpoint or on a wide surface.

But suppose da Vinci was wrong? Suppose the larger area in contact increased the friction and, therefore, the pulling power, or tractive effort, of the locomotive? L. K. Sillcox of the New York Air Brake Company had made some experiments suggesting this was so.

Throwing da Vinci into the wastebasket, Dilworth assumed that greater contact would increase friction. Using this assumption, plus a fairly well-known principle that as you increase the load the friction increases somewhat less than half as fast, Dilworth corrected the thirteen European formulas and discovered that the answers came out very close together.

These corrections put the finger on the criminal and solved the case. Thirteen accusing fingers pointed to the versatile genius who had painted "Mona Lisa." Dilworth was now able to build his own formula to forecast the performance of a lighter or heavier axle loading and a larger or smaller wheel diameter.

"I tried the formula," Dilworth says, "on the Australian locomotive and the Military Railway Switcher, and the formula forecast their slipping performance within 2 per cent. So I believe it had some value."

This slipping point was something that had to be known before the locomotive was completed, in order to determine how large a motor to put on the axle. Dilworth found a way to forecast it through a combination of deduction, creative imagination, and a willingness to question an engineering assumption that went back to Leonardo da Vinci. His discovery caused the rewriting of portions of the engineering textbooks. But he still doesn't believe that his formula is gospel.

The Jeep

A friend of Dilworth's has said that Dilworth seldom goes around a railroad terminal for fear the Diesel locomotives idling there will leave the track to jump on Dick and paw him and lick his face. This is a way of saying that, if a locomotive were animate, it would show the same affection toward its design chief as a dog would show toward a wise and sympathetic trainer. Certainly this is true of the foreign and military locomotives, but these were merely curtain raisers to his creation of what was to become Electro-Motive's most recent best seller, the General Purpose, or Jeep, the final major chore of almost a half century of productive engineering.

The GP came into being because of a postwar demand for a locomotive with characteristics not quite met by any existing EMD model. The railroads wanted a handy all-round unit, simpler and less expensive than the regular passenger and freight locomotives. Such an engine would be able to drop a train on the main line, do some work on a sidetrack, go back and pick up the train, and get it in the clear to carry out a meet order. It would be able to handle way work around a station, which meant that it would have to go easily in both directions, without inconvenience to the man in the cab. It might be hooked onto a work train or a wreck train. Though EMD had developed freight, passenger, and specialized locomotives that could do most of the work of the railroads, none of them could economically meet all these demands.

Since the regular engineering department was already overloaded with the multiple tasks of modifying existing models, the task of developing a general-purpose locomotive fell to Advanced Engineering. Dilworth welcomed the assignment because he felt that it represented EMD's golden opportunity to complete the Dieselization of American railroads.

As he saw it, the 30,000 miles of main line were already Dieselized. These miles carried half the ton-miles of all the freight movement of the country, and here the conquest was complete. At the other end of the scale, the 70,000 miles of branch line were partly Dieselized, but they carried only 2 per cent of the freight and didn't count for much. The big opportunity for locomotive sales was on the 130,000 miles of secondary line that carried the other half of the freight tonnage.

Dilworth knew that the railroads traditionally bought locomotives for their main lines, then downgraded them to secondary and branch as they grew old and obsolete. EMD had already attempted to combat this habit by turning out a branch-line locomotive, but this model had some of the appearance of the regular main-line models; so it too found its way onto the main line. This didn't discourage Dilworth.

"In planning the GP," he says, "I had two dreams. The first was to make a locomotive so ugly in appearance that no railroad would want it on the main line or anywhere near headquarters, but would keep it out as far as possible in the back country, where it could do really useful work. My second dream was to make it so simple in construction and so devoid of Christmas-tree ornaments and other whimsey that the price would be materially below our standard main-line freight locomotives."

To achieve these twin dreams, Dilworth used the standard freight unit of 1,500 horsepower and gave it a body something like a switch engine. He gave it all the necessary machinery so that it would function as well as a main-line freight locomotive, but he didn't bother about appearance at all. Look at it today, and you see that the bluntly rounded nose is gone. There is no sleek portholed car body hiding the machinery. The housing of the machinery stands out in the open, stark and businesslike and may be reached by a catwalk on either side, like a switch engine.

Because he hoped that his unlovely creature would find its

way onto secondary lines, he introduced what he calls a trick of control by which the engineer feels an instant response the moment he opens the throttle. This was different from main-line locomotives in which there was no response until the generator had poured enough power into the traction motors to start them turning. Getting an instant response wasn't important or even advisable on the main line where trains were a hundred or more cars long, but it would be useful on the secondary where trains were shorter and where the locomotive had to do a variety of jobs. But chiefly it was useful because it gave the engineer confidence. He knew that the engine was going to go to work for him, right now.

"When he opened the throttle," Dilworth says, "I wanted him to feel it in the seat of his pants."

This and other innovations made the GP a unique locomotive, but it was the location and arrangement of the cab that won the hearts of the railroads as much as any one thing. Dilworth didn't put engineer and fireman in front, as in the main-line models. He placed them about two-thirds of the way back, with some of the machinery in front and some behind. Thus, whichever way the engineer was running it, he was looking out past a nose, as he had always done in steam.

Then Dilworth had another bright idea. Before settling on the arrangement of the cab, he built a wooden mockup, windows and all, and invited engineers from the railroads to sit in it and tell him where to put controls, seats, armrests, and other devices that affected the operator.

The arrangement adopted as the result of this cooperative effort, plus some timely suggestions by Jimmy Hilton, permitted the engineer to run the locomotive equally well in either direction without having to move to another operating station on the other side of the cab. Whichever way he was going, he could conveniently handle the controls, look out the window, and see the signals.

This locomotive, the GP, went from Advanced Engineering to the regular engineering department, underwent the necessary modifications, was offered to the railroads and put into production. It was a hit from the start.

Certain intangibles had much to do with its popularity. Aside from the fact that it cost less, here was a locomotive that looked like an old and half-forgotten friend. After some years of living inside the strange and wonderful efficiency of the streamlined Diesel, old-timers found it a comfort to return to something rememberable. It was like old home week to get into the cab of the GP. It was a locomotive cab. There was a front end, whichever way you looked. You were no longer perched in front and atop several thousand pulsating horses, you were behind them.

"It was a tool," says Hilton, "that fitted the railroad man's hand."

Actually, it was basically the regular freight unit that EMD had been making for over ten years, stripped down to its functional parts. Yet railroads everywhere echoed the sentiment of one assistant superintendent of motive power who told Jimmy Hilton: "There isn't anything that locomotive won't do or can't do any time of the day or night."

It was ugly all right. Ugly, unpretentious, and businesslike. And it became the modern best seller in the EMD line.

Yet it proved to be Dilworth's greatest disappointment. He had hoped it would be the key that would unlock the door to the secondary lines. Instead, like all other new locomotives, it was bought principally for the main line, there to serve until the day when newer and shinier descendants would relegate it to the service for which it had been originally planned.

Aside from the planning of the GP, Dilworth's Advanced Engineering Department laid out rough plans for foreign locomotives, using as many standard American parts as possible. Locomotives intended for Israeli, the Scandinavian countries, Newfoundland, and Brazil were started in Advanced Engineering and carried to completion elsewhere. The department was also given the job of initiating foreign engineers into the mysteries of Diesel-electric operation.

Early in 1950 Dilworth retired from Electro-Motive and for the next two years served the division as independent consultant. In 1952 he took home his slide rules for good, leaving to others the job of laying out and improving the locomotives that will soon complete the Dieselization of the railroads.

Dilworth's home in Hinsdale, the pleasant Chicago suburb not far from La Grange, is a spacious house of stone and white siding, large enough to accommodate his four married children and their families, should they all descend on the senior Dilworths for Thanksgiving or Christmas. Dilworth designed it himself on laundry cardboards because the architect insisted on building the kind of house he wanted, not the kind Dilworth wanted.

The house is unostentatious, yet purposeful, like the man, and it has a quiet charm, like Mrs. Dilworth. There's a screened porch overlooking the rear lawn, where the two spend much of their time. There's a library containing books without fancy bindings but with a variety of titles that indicates a wide and endless curiosity. There's a workshop downstairs for tinkering. On the basement wall is an autographed picture of Dr. Herman Lemp, the electrical wizard and one-time associate of Thomas Edison, to whom Dilworth turned constantly during his early rail-car days at G.E.

The Dilworths like to take off in their car, without notice, possibly for their property on Vashon Island in Puget Sound not far from where Dick was born, or possibly for their recently acquired land on a lake in the Ozarks. When they travel, they take to the back roads because, Dilworth says, life comes closer to the edge of a back road than it does to a superhighway.

Though ostensibly retired, Dilworth has the capacity and the intellectual restlessness to remain forever occupied, whether in the fashioning of a toy for the grandchildren or working in the garden. Now and then he likes to recall things.

If you're with him at those times, you're privileged to sit in on a rare session of yarn-spinning and sheer fun. His face is a magnet that holds you, with its bold nose, high-arched brows, and eyes that are mostly turned inward toward a thought, but occasionally are aimed at you with disconcerting directness. His pipe is in action at all times, either between his lips or suffering punishment on the edge of a large glass ashtray. Worrying the pipe is an accompaniment to his thought processes. He uses it to organize his memories. And he has more to remember than most men:

Since 1910, forty-two years before, Dilworth had spent most of his working life proving that internal combustion could haul trains. He became a dedicated man as soon as he saw the first gas-electric rail car. When he came to Hamilton's struggling company in January, 1926, Jimmy Hilton testifies that a "steady hand took hold of the engineering development of the rail car, and there was a clear court of decision for every knotty problem." When the rail car reached its limit of usefulness, Dilworth produced the pioneer passenger locomotives that made steam obsolete on the main line, and he followed these with the powerful workhorses that broke the freight bottlenecks of World War II. These miracles were wrought by a man who had only one-half day of formal schooling in his life.

He forever keeps reducing the job of proportioning a locomotive to simple terms. First, he says, you decide how heavy it has to be, and this is determined by the load you have to pull and the steepest grade you have to climb. Then you decide how many wheels you need to carry the load. Finally you find out how fast you have to go, and you have your horsepower. And all this can be done by simple arithmetic— and a slide rule. Perhaps it's true, as one associate says, that "Dilworth was always making the problem simple so that he could understand it himself."

From the first rail car down to the GP, Dilworth has been stubborn in his battle against the men who wanted to incorporate their pet ideas into the locomotive, whether it was a cast-steel underframe, a special coupler, or an electrical control. No matter how good the item was in itself, Dilworth didn't want it unless it was a good part of the Diesel locomotive.

Dilworth has a story to illustrate what he believes to be

his most important contribution. Relaxing in the pleasant
screened porch of his home, he points at the fence surround-
ing his rear lawn and garden. Before beginning, he bangs his
pipe on the edge of a huge ashtray.

"If you wanted a fence for the yard, there," he says, talking
through lips partly closed over his pipestem, "and asked a
plumber to build it, he'd make it out of pipe and couplings.
If you asked a carpenter to build it, he'd use wood and nails.
Give the job to a blacksmith, and he'd probably weld it, and
a bricklayer would use mortar. It's a good idea to have a man
around who is interested in none of these special arts, but
is interested in the fence."

THE DILWORTH CALENDAR

1885, March 6	Born in Seattle, Washington.
1897, Fall	Received first and only half day of formal schooling.
1897–1904	Wandered over much of the world, picking up the trade of machinist.
1904, Fall	Enlisted as electrician in the Navy.
1909, May	Discharged from the Navy as a chief electrician.
1910	Hired by General Electric as a machinist.
1910, July	Introduced to the G.E. rail car, powered by a gasoline engine that generated electricity to turn traction motors. Hence, known as a gas-electric. As machinist on the test floor, helped develop a new and larger gasoline engine for the rail car.
1911	Delivered rail cars to the railroads.
1911–1912	Served as road foreman of rail-car jockeys in Middle Western plains region.
1912, February 20	Married Ada Edwards of Bryn Mawr, Pennsylvania.
1913	As experimental-floor foreman at G.E., helped develop the first Diesel engines designed and built in the United States. Con-

tributed many details of design to these prototypes.

1926, January 1   Became chief engineer of Electro-Motive
Corporation.

1927–1930   With Winton Engine Company developed
series of gasoline engines, each more powerful than the last.

1929–1931   With Winton Engine Company developed
a 900-horsepower distillate burner for Santa
Fe.

1930–1931   Designed radical new air-brake system for
Santa Fe power car, taking the master air
cylinder off the bottom of the car, breaking
it up into smaller air cylinders, and placing
these on the trucks. This is now standard
practice.

1933–1935   Designed the power cars for the first streamliners—the *City* trains of Union Pacific and
the *Zephyrs* of the Burlington.

1934–1935   Designed the first commercially successful
Diesel-electric passenger locomotives, housing them in a simple four-axle box-car-type
power car.

1938–1939   With the aid of a growing engineering staff,
designed and built the first successful Diesel-
electric freight locomotives.

1942   Designed a gearbox with four clutches to
enable four Diesel engines to turn a single
propeller shaft. Some 3,500 of these Quad
engines used to power LCIs during war.

1947–1948   Designed special locomotive with light axle
loading for Australia. With Martin Blom-
berg, designed a three-axle, or bogie, truck
for the Australian locomotive that had 40
per cent more tractive effort than conven-
tional truck.

1948–1949   Developed a military railway switcher for
             U.S. Army, a universal locomotive that could
             be used in all types of weather and adjusted
             to any gauge track.

1949–1950   Designed the General Purpose (Jeep) loco-
             motive that has since become Electro-Mo-
             tive's best seller.

1950   Retired from Electro-Motive but continued
             to serve as consultant.

1952   Complete retirement at age sixty-seven.

Franklin M. Reck spent the first half of his writing career as an author of fiction and articles for boys, and for five years was managing editor of The American Boy, once the most popular youth magazine in the country.

His technical writing began with a series of popularized histories of the automobile, transportation, radio, and power. Three of these books were selections of the Junior Literary Guild.

His free-lance career began in 1941, when he bought a house and seven acres in Manchester, among the hills of southern Michigan. During the war he served as field editor for an aviation publication.

Since the war he has written two corporation histories—On Time, the story of the Electro-Motive Division of General Motors, and Sand in Their Shoes, the history of American Steel Foundries. In between, he wrote The 4-H Story, official history of the 4-H movement. An ardent trout fisherman, he has written many outdoor stories, mostly of explorations in the Ontario bush.

During his writing of On Time, he had frequent contact with an unusual man, a brilliant, self-educated engineer with an unfettered imagination, Richard McLean Dilworth. He undertook the assignment to write Dilworth's story with enthusiasm, not only because of the man, but because Dilworth's life reveals a revolution in railroading.

Reck is a graduate in journalism from Iowa State College, and served variously in steel mills, machine-tool plants, and the Army before settling down to a typewriter.